The Little White Book on Race

Also by Judi Culbertson and Patti Bard,
with illustrations by Susan Perl

Games Christians Play

The Little White Book on Race

Judi Culbertson
and Patti Bard

Drawings by Susan Perl

J. B. Lippincott Company
Philadelphia & New York

Preface

Welcome to the White Trumpet Anthology! *White Trumpet* Magazine, as everyone knows, is the unfailing Voice of Today's Racial Moderate.

It used to be simple enough, back in the days when black was black and white was safe, to recognize someone trying to stir up trouble and merely identify him: "Do-gooder! Liberal! Social Gospelite! Commie!"

Today, however, no one will admit to any of the old names. Even the most fanatic and racially suspect will claim:

"Well, I'm no *do-gooder.* . . ."

"I certainly couldn't be classified as a liberal. . . ." *

Even the grand old designation "Social Gospel" has fallen into disrepute.

Although "Commie" still carries potent undertones, it has not generally been considered in good taste for

* Like Samuel Whitehope, the old-time liberal, who insisted that the Negroes under his care at the sit-in wear white shirts and ties and carry Plato or the Bible while integrating Lester's Redneck Beanery. He suffered a severe loss of faith when one belched at an unseemly moment.

friendly use since the Peabody–Housedress affair: The day Mrs. Peabody called Mrs. Housedress and said, "Hello there, you probably don't know *me* but I was wondering if you would be able to make a set of simple curtains for the dayroom at the new Child Care Center. I'm enlisting the help of everyone in—"

And Mrs. Housedress growled, "I don't even know how to sew, Commie!"

"What?"

"You heard me, you silly dupe. You're an unwitting part of a Red plot to make them think they're as good as we are! Give them curtains, they'll want windows next. Dirty Pink-o!" Bang.

But it didn't end there. Mrs. Peabody also happened to be the Mayor's wife and a Racial Moderate in Lady Bountiful guise, who didn't sleep well until Mrs. Housedress had been tittered and scorned out of town.

At any rate, "Commie" has been relegated to the poor-taste category in name-calling, along with "Nigger lover" and "Nut."

Still, even though the use of names may have deteriorated, people can still be judged against the standard of what we, as Racial Moderates, are.

To the right of us are those misguided people who must solve their racial tensions by lynching Negroes or throwing fire bombs whenever they step out of place. While we can understand their reasons and sympathize with them, we cannot endorse such violent solutions. No; our position as Racial Moderates is sensible; it is reasoned out and sane. We are able to see both sides of a question and realize that many times it is better to keep silent and

let things work out by themselves than go blundering into areas where we do not know all the facts—unless of course it is a matter of defending something threatened that we hold dear. We realize that the prevailing system *must* reflect the feelings of the majority of the people, and it is hardly likely that a majority would be wrong. If the agitators would only stop making trouble, stirring things up, we would be able to work it all out calmly, sensibly, and without tears.

Everyone to the left of us is a fanatic.

Their minds have become unhinged on this particular subject, their perspective badly distorted in relation to the rest of life's issues. While such fanatics *can* be dangerous, most can be kept in line by an adroit combination of frustrated goals and threats. In short, we realize that in an increasingly mad and corrupt world, ours is the Voice of Moderation and Sanity.

Ours is the voice that must be heeded. We are kind to the unfortunate and insane—but we do not give them freedom to wreck the world. And that is what this anthology is all about.

Its purpose, like that of our monthly magazine, is threefold. Not only do we strive to entertain and instruct by articles and regular features concerned with this very important area, we also attempt to offer help and concrete suggestions for readers caught in particular racial dilemmas. Too, we supply moral support by giving an opportunity for readers to communicate with the rest of our constituency by stating problems or supplying solutions; at the very least to be reassured of how many others there are "out there" like them!

This anthology is made up of the most significant, most entertaining, and most helpful articles and features of the *White Trumpet* in the last few years. What more can we say? Except—

Read it in good health!

The Editors

Contents

11

The Little White Book on Race

Tilly Tupple—
The Traitor No One
Would Suspect

by JANE E. REDEYE

I knew who it was as soon as I heard her voice on the phone, for Elvira Wifflespin is the well-known wife of the beloved Percy Wifflespin, Jr., owner of several thousand shares of blue-chip stock and creator of the captivating business slogan "I'll Hire Who I Damn Well Please." She is a respected teacher and citizen in her own right. It was, in fact, about a crisis in her teaching that she called me. I quickly agreed to meet her at the Ivory Palace Restaurant. Over our chocolate eclairs, she told me her story:

"Little did I suspect that Tilly Tupple, my own teacher's aide in my own second-grade classroom, would be a traitor! I had always thought of Tilly as an acceptable woman. She is forty-two years old, wears her dresses below the knee, and has never so much as gone near a civil rights demonstration. She seemed to carry out her little duties at school adequately enough, and she knew enough to stay out of the Faculty Room."

"Tell me what happened," I encouraged her.

"We have, as you know, a very nice little school in a town safely away from the turmoil of the city. We do have Negroes but hardly any race problem. I have several colored children in my own class whom I have easily been able to contain. One little boy is a perfectly terrible child whose father is *in absentia* and whose mother is dead or something. He lives with an aunt who goes out of the house to work at some low-caste job two hours before school begins, leaving the boy free to do any kind of damage he pleases. When he arrives in my class he is extremely sloppily dressed, apt to be chewing disgusting-looking scraps of food, apt to be tearful and sleepy. He requires a special firmness from me, as you can imagine, since his presence is so disturbing to our nice children. I handle him well, I must say."

Mrs. Wifflespin choked a little on her whipped cream and continued, "Two months ago, however, when I was checking on a new social studies teacher with a beard, I came back to my classroom to find my trusted aide off in the corner with this little boy. She was smiling at him and they were talking together in low tones. I was shocked, but I vowed to be tolerant of her. Gradually I came to notice that she wasted more and more time with this child—helping him draw, reading stories with him, and, most disconcerting, simply talking with him when she *could* have been emptying my wastebasket.

16

"Then the crisis came," she said tensely. "It was eleven thirty on an ordinary Tuesday. I told the class that everyone who wanted to buy a Dixie Cup for lunch must get out his nickel and go to stand in the Ice Cream Line. The bad little boy I have been telling you about began to go all through his pockets looking for his money. Supposedly. At that point another child in the class—a darling little girl who wears a perky new hairbow each and every day—came up and said she had lost her nickel. Just as I was lending her one, that *other* child came right up to my desk and said the same thing!"

"You mean," I asked her, "he told you he lost his nickel, expecting you to lend *him* one?"

"Yes, indeed. First of all, I doubt that he would have ever had the audacity to do such a thing had he not been encouraged by the aide to step out of place. He used to know better. I know, second of all, that he was lying. He never had a nickel in the first place. I ordered him, gently but firmly, to go stand facing the wall as punishment. Then I happened to see my aide, Miss Tupple, with her purse open and a nickel in her hand ready to lend him. 'Put that money *away*,' I said, but, still my tolerant self, I drew her aside and attempted to explain to her the reasoning behind my order. It was then that I became entirely disillusioned with Miss Tilly Tupple."

Mrs. Wifflespin remembered her conversation with Tilly Tupple word for word, and here it is just as she reported it to me:

Mrs. W.: Do you know that child and his aunt get money from *Welfare?*

17

TILLY: Yes.

Mrs. W.: Do you know what that means?

TILLY: Yes.

MRS. W.: Of course you do. It means that he has been taught since infancy to get something for nothing, and to constantly practice deceit in getting it. Don't you think you give *enough* out of your hard-earned wage without giving him *ice cream* on top of it?

TILLY: No.

MRS. W.: Do you realize that if I had let you give him a nickel today, he would ask you for a nickel every single day from now on?

TILLY: No.

MRS. W.: Will you at least consider the matter and attempt to learn a very valuable lesson from this experience?

TILLY (*in a frightening growl*): You *bet* I will.

Mrs. Wifflespin's hand shook as she raised her coffee to her lips. "Her tone was not only insubordinate; it was ominous. I stood aghast, wondering what Percy would have done had he heard her." She leaned toward me and added, "Besides, I'm relatively sure she slipped the little creature the nickel when the Ice Cream Line was moving between the East Girls' Room and the cafeteria door."

As a tenacious reporter I went to Miss Tupple's neighborhood and dug into her background. There seemed to be no ready cause for her misguided attitudes. From a limited socio-economic background she was, according to her neighbors, an example of one who had raised her-

self by her own bootstraps without a helping hand from anybody. Certainly it seemed she ought to have felt that Negroes should do the same.

I talked personally with Tilly Tupple in her own neat little house. She had just returned from a meeting of the Ladies' Missionary Society. Looking as harmless as a middle-aged cream puff, she told me, "I just hate oppression. I just think every person ought to have the right to *live*. I can't do much, but whatever little thing I can do to see people get a chance to live—well, I'm going to do it."

Before I could ask her just what little things she planned to do next, she said, "The thing that bothers me is that when a black person looks at me going by on the street, he probably thinks he is seeing a Mrs. Wifflespin. I'm *not* a Mrs. Wifflespin; I'm Tilly Tupple. But a black person just seeing me isn't likely to know I'm even here."

I left Miss Tupple's house to consult with an outstand-

19

ing authority on race relations who prefers to remain nameless for this article. I had a question for him: *What can we do with whites like Tilly Tupple?* He told me that Tilly herself had given the clue. We must make sure, he affirmed, that black people *never* know Tilly is "even here." Our duty is to encourage the idea among Negroes that all whites think alike—more or less like Mrs. Wifflespin. This, he assured me, is not a difficult matter, particularly as it pertains to inarticulate and powerless people like Tilly Tupple.

Hastily the authority wrote on a piece of paper and handed it to me. "Put this in your article," he said. The paper read:

Follow this logic carefully:

1. If all Negroes believe that all whites are Mrs. Wifflespins, sooner or later Tilly Tupple is likely to get bonked on the head by an angry darkie.

2. Tilly Tupple will then see the error of her ways, and know Negroes for what they are.

Also:

1. If all Negroes believe that all whites are Mrs. Wifflespins *and*

2. It should come to a riot in the center of town, Tilly Tupple will be right in the white line of fire whilst Mrs. Wifflespin remains safe in her large house on the hill outside of town. Thus do we preserve Mrs. Wifflespin and let nature take its course with Tilly Tupple.

And remember:

If she keeps slipping nickels and otherwise upsetting the status quo (by word or deed), no people are easier to threaten or fire than the Tilly Tupples of this world, who

21

work by the hour and are unacquainted with persons of influence.

Touched by his concern, I thanked him effusively and reached for the phone to reassure Elvira Wifflespin.

Shaken Beliefs

Each month in the White Trumpet *we run a feature known as "Shaken Beliefs." In this section our readers write in and tell us how a particular belief they have held all their lives has been suddenly shown up as "untrue."* *

Here are reprinted a collection of the more significant of these during the past year.

A NATURAL INFERIORITY COMPLEX

"I was never so surprised in my life," wrote Mrs. A.G. of Green, Minnesota, "as when I found out that some colored people actually believe that they are as capable as we are and sometimes even more so! I always supposed they had a natural inferiority complex based on some kind of scientific finding, but during the Green Cookie Push I worked with a girl who thought it was only natural that she sit up on the platform with the Mayor and accept all the congratulations while *I* was slaving away in the Almond Goody booth! When I found her and questioned her about this inequality, she just smiled and said, 'Give us an inch and we'll take a mile. . . .' "

* This does not mean that they *are,* in fact, untrue, but simply that there will always be people trying to tear down the structures of our society.

UTTERLY DUMFOUNDED

Mr. N.O.P. of Casper, New York, who has a solid history of trying to get Negroes into the same building trades unions (on a suitable level, of course, we are sure) as he is, was utterly dumfounded when he found out last week that "they *aren't* grateful up north for all we've done for them. However, that doesn't mean I'll stop trying to—"

CALLED CHARLIE SCROOGE

Explains Mr. P.B.L. of Blanket, Alabama, "I have been reading your magazine faithfully for years and enjoying it, and I want to tell you that it came as a rude shock to me, even with your hints, to find out firsthand that colored folks do not invariably love and revere white folks. I've been hiring coons for seventy years with no trouble until last week, when one uppity nigger whose pay I refused to raise to ninety cents an hour informed me that they all call me Charlie Scrooge and 'hate my guts.' Now I ask you, is that any way for coons to treat an Old Southern Gentleman they are supposed to love and revere? I had to take to bed for a week afterward while they were being systematically chastised for insolence."

"NATIVE AMERICANS!"

Miss K.P. of Devilswood, Arizona, writes about how a friend of hers ran into a troupe of Negro Gospel singers who travel around the country who "just because they

had been around for 350 years thought of themselves as 'Southerners' and 'native Americans' even more than us people who really are!"

(*Editor's Note: What will they think of next?*)

NOT AS INTELLIGENT?

In an experience similar to Mrs. A.G.'s of Green, Minnesota, Mr. A.Z. of Trump, California, reports on a belief he had always assumed was true, "that though there may be a few good baseball players and bright mutants among Negroes, on the average they are less intelligent than we are. I found out differently when a Mexican Negro in my company who had been in my class at U.C.L.A. was actually promoted before me; when I demanded to know why, I was told that he synthesized material better and was more capable in other ways. Now I'm really wondering."

(*Editor's Note: Wonder no more; the exception always exists merely to prove the rule.*)

ONE VERY WICKED MAN

Miss B.B., a college student from Alligator, Florida, who had always been properly taught as to how immoral Negroes were, found out that 85 per cent of them have some white blood in them. After some puzzled wondering as to just where they had gotten it from, she wrote, "I realized that they could have been genetically responsible for only fifty per cent of the immorality. Which either means that there were some pretty immoral white people running around then too, or else one very strong-gened and wicked man. . . ."

And now, to close, this final shattered belief that belongs to my wife: "I never knew *they* had white palms and soles on their feet. Now whenever I see one I feel all funny toward them; because there's nothing strange like that about *me,* and I had just assumed *they* were black all over."

He Came to Cause Us Trouble!

A true experience

by HEGEL B. MISCONCEPT

He looked normal. Usually he wore a suit and a tie, and there was even a bit of distinguished gray at his temples. But actually he was a raging fanatic who came to plot against us. And he came disguised as a man of the cloth. Until a few days ago, he was the minister of our church!

Just before he left town he made a final attempt to demoralize us by insinuating that we were hopelessly uneducated and unenlightened. I want first to explain who we *really* are, and then I shall recount what this man tried to do to us.

We are not dumb people. We are members of the upper-middle section of the middle class—people who read condensed books and enjoy dignified services when we are in church. We are not like the common churchmen:

we have often spent time (right in the church-school classes) thinking about race relations, current interest rates, and other practical issues. Here is a short outline on what we believe about race to show how thoroughly we think things through:

1. Human beings are not all *that* guilty for the way things are. Man can't do much about history, as all of us who read books realize.

2. History has caused things like segregation and under-privileged classes, and now all of us are conditioned to them. This makes the race problem for both blacks and whites very very very very complicated. One just can't get up and start doing something about it because of all that history and conditioning.

3. Nonetheless we would be willing to cooperate with any sound and sane racial program based on a view of how complex and limited the action must be in the light of history. . . .

4. But all of us have complete faith that history flows just like a river and eventually will work itself out fine, and everything will get better. For instance, look at how the situations of the black man and the masses have improved through the years. We believe our principal responsibility is to let history work itself out.

Unlike us, the minister is one of those persons who thoughtlessly bring trouble to others—and himself. He was, for example, one of the people who went down there in the South and campaigned for civil rights back before many Negroes even were active. He later worked on voter registration, getting himself shot at when he should have

been home earning a living for his family.

We hired him partly because we did not know his whole history and partly because we thought he had reformed. Within a month he was talking about open housing on our local radio station. Our local station carries a meditation program which the clergy of the town take turns leading. Quite naturally there is a bit of good-natured competition to see whose minister can give the nicest-sounding meditation. The competitive spirit especially asserts itself (in an entirely Christian manner) in a little unspoken contest between our church, which is known for being calm and liberal, and the church down the street. The church down the street is pastored by a cocky fundamentalist type and is known for being noisy and nitpicking. The day before it was our minister's turn to give the meditation, the fundamentalist fellow from the other church surprised us by giving a radio talk that out-calmed everybody in town. His text was Corinthians 5 and his subject was "love tempered with sanity." The gist of it was that if one lives the Christian life, he will be fearless and prosperous—and he put it beautifully.

The very next day *our* minister sat in front of the microphone, took the same text, and began a diatribe on open housing, citing specific neighborhoods that ought to be open-housed. Some of us live in those neighborhoods.

As practicing Christians, we reasoned that he had not been in our community long enough to know what was expected of him, and we decided to say nothing to him— to, as the saying goes, give him a chance. It was a mistake we shall never repeat. Hardly before we realized what was happening, his plot had nearly destroyed us. First he hired a *white* janitor. Then he formed a coalition of concerned community churchmen—51.03 per cent of them were Negro! Next he sweet-talked the emotional ladies on the Music Commission into selecting a choir director who made the choir practice too hard. She was dark brown.

Stunned, we watched as he omitted the sermon one day * and instead invited one of the 51.03 per cent to take the pulpit and talk about what Christians can do to work for equality. I remember sitting in the congregation, sensing with fear the confusion and agitation this brought to some of our younger members.

* He omitted sermons too often, anyway, and substituted odd, experimental innovations which were in poor taste. But that is another subject.

30

That was not the end of it. He seemed to have money of his own, suspicious indeed for a minister of the gospel, and he began to co-sign mortgages with Negroes. At Christmas his three grown children came home for vacation. We found the situation unbelievable: these children were all adopted, and two of them were the wrong color.

Finally he drew up a plan to unite with the Negro church over on Pone Street.

It was then I realized for the first time that the solidarity of our church membership had been almost irreparably eroded by this man. Our church has 200 members, and somehow he had commandeered 175 members' names for his petition on the church union. The "we" of this article—the voices and minds of sanity—had dwindled to 25 members. The Lord only knows how many members of the Negro church he led astray. They tend to be naïve about black separatism.

When I confronted him, he said his was "the most moderate plan anybody could think of" and he hoped it would be carried out forthwith. He did not reckon on the power of an angry minority.

Can you imagine how I and the other 24 no-saying members of our church felt? We felt

—Oppressed!

—Forced into something that would affect our whole way of living!

—Unrepresented in the society!

—Downgraded!

—Pushed in the corner!

We didn't like being a minority that got walked all over. *Who would?*

31

My story has a happy ending, however, because we were a well-heeled minority. We may have had one-eighth of the vote, but we had seven-eighths of the money. Fighting his plot with a plot of our own, we resolved to save the church. The 25 of us met at my house one night and burned our pledge cards. It was not a crass demonstration, such as wild youngsters hold, but a dignified little ceremony followed by a brandy toast. We could feel that the warmth of our strength and unity would spread to the other members—and we were right.

The other 175 members, ultimately persuaded—as I have mentioned—about the flow of history, weren't in a mood to put 15 per cent of their salaries where their vote was. Rather than see a fine church become a denomination-supported mission with no heat in the nave, a reconstituted and very strong majority of our 200 members decided to:

1. Put in effect a new set of Rules and Regulations for the minister.

2. Order the disbanding of the concerned churchmen.

3. Fire the overdemanding choir director.

4. Void the plan for church union.

He came to cause us trouble, this man disguised as a minister of God. But he resigned last Friday.

And we are almost back to normal already.

Unbeatable Tactics

Regular readers of the White Trumpet *are quick to turn to the "Unbeatable Tactics" offered in each issue of the magazine. Selected for placement throughout the anthology are several of the year's most popular tactics. Without the cooperation of many individuals and institutions, the job of our "UT" editor would be an impossible one. The magazine extends a hardy "thank you" to those who have so generously contributed their ideas.*

THE GREAT PULPIT EXCHANGE

Contributed by the Reverend Simon W. Sloth of Solid Suburbia Church

"Well, once a year I take *his* pulpit and I preach to *them* just as though they were my own people, and I shake hands after the service, too.

"And once a year I try to have *him* come here and take my pulpit. Last year I went to a lot of trouble to arrange things so that he took my pulpit on the Sunday nearest the anniversary of Martin Luther King's death, which my Board thought was a very nice gesture indeed.

"As one who is thus deeply involved, I find that I have a firsthand insight into racial relations in this area, and I can tell you that they are simply first-rate!

33

"Is there anything else you want to know?"

I WAS ALL FOR IT—UNTIL

Memorize the following and repeat it whenever the occasion arises:

"I was all for racial equality, though I never said much about it one way or the other, until those Negroes and Puerto Ricans at the colleges pulled their tricks with their guns. Now I say if any of 'em will do such a thing, all of 'em will do it if they get the chance. And now I say— just don't talk to me about racial equality, or I'll talk to you about those Negroes and their guns!"

Coping in the Church

An editorial report

by J. J. UPTIGHT,
Associate Editor
P. F. PRUDENCE,
Assistant Associate Editor

Though many difficult problems are faced by
the white man in his everyday life, several of his racial
concerns may be involved with his life in the church.
The Christian's priority here should be to keep things
the way they are. If fanatics and agitators make preserv-
ing the status quo impossible, then the next best thing is
to face the present and the future with a plan. Plans, of
course, should be formed so that they make the present
and the future as comfortable as possible by foiling the
misguided ones of our age who have gone mad. To aid
today's concerned Christian we traveled to several towns
and cities in the United States, talking with people who
know how to cope. Compiled here are helpful descrip-
tions of the plans and projects we discovered. Group A
relates directly to the threat of the interracial church. We
found that there are still assorted blacks and whites who

want to "integrate" churches; plans presented in Group A may serve as models for our readers in dealing with them. Group B relates to more general matters of morals and action.

GROUP A

Fighting with Fright: To Willard Kreep, things looked black indeed. Dismayed and outvoted, he watched as members of his White Presbyterian Church and the Black Presbyterian Church down the road completed plans for church union. Unbelievingly he saw the denominational headquarters was not only lending verbal support to these upstarts; it was also lending them money to build a new Christian education facility. At the last minute, in a burst of faith, Mr. Kreep brought in a group of Black Leopards demanding ten billion dollars in reparations, to show White Presbyterians "what it would really be like."

The Food Basket: This plan has often been successfully employed by Binder Methodist Church in Asphalt, Arkansas. Whenever a Negro family visits their church, members present the family with a food basket and a carton of missionary-barrel-type clothes . . . making sure first that they don't need them. They have other ways of dealing with genuinely poor Negro families (such as seating them on the front steps).

The Pet Negro: Brindle Baptist in Brotherlove, Pennsylvania is to be emulated for integrating the local church with just one Negro. They pay him royally to do the

janitorial work and treat him so well that he discourages all other blacks from coming there for fear of losing his unique status and privileges.

The Sensible Thing to Do: Good Neighbors Congregational Church is reconciled to a changing future—but to a future in which they constructively control the changes. They have enrolled a smooth and polished black dentist as unofficial Negro Membership Chairman. His job is to get other smooth and polished Negroes into the church—and to keep niggers out of it. (*Note:* The polished dentist has offered similar services for the housing development where several GNCC members live. In an impressive expression of good faith, the homeowning churchmen therefore allowed the dentist to sign for a lot last Monday.)

GROUP B

Doing Our Bit: Nobody likes feeling guilty. The people of St. Agatha's Church in Twinge, New York, are no exception. They maintain a clapboard, roach-infested shack in Georgia that they call a "social mission." Without decreasing the entertainment allowance of their rector or increasing anybody's pledges, St. Aggie's finds that it is possible to staff this mission with the young communicants who made them feel guilty in the first place. These youthful idealists are paid some $60 a month as the Lord provides. Since they are much better off down in Georgia than they would be if they stayed home and made damn nuisances of themselves in the parish, two birds are nicely clonked with one handy stone.

38

Saving Negroes: "Saving" is good for the Negro, since he will have Heaven to look forward to, and good for the Christian white who saves him—since a star in the crown is awarded for every person whom one leads to salvation. (To be sure, one cannot expect the same size star for a common black as one would receive for the Vice President of the United States, but a star is a star nonetheless.) An added benefit of saving Negroes is this: people long have been known for becoming, on salvation, immediately nonviolent, loving, and generous to a fault. If we could only get all the Negroes saved so that they were exactly like white fundamentalists, there would be no more strife in the world.

"Saving" can be effective as it was practiced by the following:

Mercy Church of Swamp, South Carolina: Along the highway not far from Mercy Church there is a string of disreputable cabins where sloppy (and doubtless immoral) Negroes live. The brave men of Mercy went out there one Sunday afternoon and tacked up tasteful road signs for a length of thirty miles reading: "God's Grace Is Free to All," and "Why Haven't YOU Believed??" and "THERE'S A RICH NEW LIFE IN JESUS." The signs, reports Mercy Deacon Harvey Whitemeat, serve two purposes because the highway is heavily used by godless tourists. "We're not only reaching the blinded black man," Whitemeat declares. "We're giving the Message to the tourists as well. When they travel our road, they find out how we feel about the Gospel in these parts."

A Group of Bunk, New Jersey, Christians: Amazed and distressed by the recent riots and other signs of ungodly malcontent there, they took radical action. "We believe," says their chairman, Myron Sweetnose, "that the problem is a *spiritual* one. 'What has a man's soul got to do with the rat in his sink?' is what we say. We truly believe that Negroes *can* get saved. To prove it, we're going out and find one who is and bring him here to put on a big salvation campaign. They ought to listen to one of their own. Unless their hearts are just too hard to melt, our plan is bound to work. In the Black Evangelism Effort, we're going to give them the Answer; it'll be their own fault if they don't take it."

The United Christocrats, as witnessed in the Big Splash Case: At its last general conference this large denomination reported a laudable expenditure of $42,000,-000.82 for the erection and operation of a twenty-three-story Race Relations Building.

Sixty-five eager photographers and painters were especially commissioned to cover the walls of the edifice with art depicting the races working together. Six hundred and fifty-eight "researchers" were hired to sit at specially purchased African mahogany desks while they study such problems as "Hominy Distribution Among the Underprivileged Minorities." Five hundred enthusiastic academicians who "know where the roll is" were awarded grants for work on projects related to racial tension. (Four hundred and ninety-seven of them are presently seminaring and conferencing on the matter at Hawaii's Blue Vista Seaside Hotel.) In fact, everybody who's anybody has his hand in the pot and his picture in the *Life*

magazine featur
tage in showing
cerned").

The result of
and down in th
ways has—or r
so successfully

Buster A. G
Communist sin
erates who feel
a Law and Or
have banded
"and got us a
of special-trai
Christianity i
there, helping
week at our
stration of th
those snarlin
people who
problem: you
about it!"

Buster may
not *in* it, bec
his church p
11 A.M., and
morning chu
us that the
leadership o
We find Mr
under the

40

41

carefully consider their own circumstances before taking such forthright measures. If too many of us become activists, we shall lose our impeccable reputation as Moderates.

We conclude this report with a note of encouragement: in this difficult age, coping in the church is not always easy—but it is usually possible. We leave with you the ingenious examples of Willard Kreep, Good Neighbors Church, St. Agatha's parish, and the others we discovered who are staying on the job.

Helpful Hints from Herman and Muriel Spot's "Color-Scheme Clinic"

A column born in the second issue of the magazine continues in the present to serve readers. Without forsaking the principles on which our periodical was founded, authors Herman and Muriel Spot practice relevancy and timeliness. Herman tackles a wide variety of today's problems, while his wife concentrates on making life a little easier for homemakers the nation over.

HOW TO KEEP YOUR GROUP
FROM LOOKING LILY WHITE

Are people calling your group a bunch of bigots? Why not try importing an African or other non-American black-skinned individual with a romantic name and accent? Such a person may lend the proper balance to your business, college, church, or service club—all without increasing American black participation and further disrupting a disrupted society.

These people are often very black, and nobody can call you a bad name when you have a very black somebody right in the middle of you. Furthermore, you are not likely to have him in the middle of you for longer than you want to because of the convenient laws on emigration.

Religious folks will find it particularly beneficial if the individual has been saved from the dark life of a primitive tribe—though he should have his hair straightened and be sent to a civilizing seminary. Others will discover that the cultural shock of color is always mitigated by a black who speaks with an Oxford or Swahili accent rather than a ghetto drawl . . . but not mitigated enough to make things dangerous.

HOW TO GRACIOUSLY DUMP

AN INSIDE AGITATOR

Everyone knows it would be hardly moderate to fire a minister (or teacher, college president, librarian, etc.) for his views on the racial dilemma. Even if he brought in a Negro assistant in one of those funny dresses and a ring through his ear, it wouldn't really be right. Even if he sold his house in the nicest neighborhood in town to a black family with thirteen children, it wouldn't be Christian to fire him for such a reason.

Therefore it is necessary to look into his life and locate

45

other reasons. And this is not as hard as it might seem at first, since few people are perfect. The most important thing, actually, having once chosen your reason, is to stick to it no matter what. Do not hesitate to make your reason public if it becomes necessary; this will help you avoid censure, since what critic, though sympathetic to his racial position, will defend a clergyman who dips into the offering plate when he runs short and never visits the sick?

If no reason comes immediately to mind, consider one of the following sample reasons:

1. *Unpatriotic* ("Refused to buy a raffle ticket for the American Legion Basket of Cheer outside the dime store")

2. *Alcoholic* ("Bought a raffle ticket for the American Legion Basket of Cheer outside the dime store")

3. *Mustache*

4. *Homosexuality, shows leanings toward* ("Was seen downtown wearing a rose shirt with a paisley handkerchief")

5. *Politics, Mixes Religion with*

6. *Sideburns, Too Long*

7. *Communism, Soft on* ("Refused to support the Youth for Decency, Patriotism, and Clean Thinking in Sex Rally, thereby giving our church a black eye in the face of the community")

8. *Of Low Moral Character* ("His daughter *had* to get married")

9. *Pornography, Advocate of* ("Was seen sneaking into a benefit performance of *Hair*")

MAID SERVICE?
(FROM THE SERIES
"HINTS ON HOUSEHOLD HELP"
BY MRS. SPOT)

Believe it or not, there are people who criticize the hiring of other human beings as cooks, maids, and cleaning ladies, even when they know full well that they are paid a living wage—in return for nothing more than a good day's work, a cheerful disposition, and a few little favors now and then. Heaven knows, in my own case it's difficult enough being a professional free-lance writer and mother of five without having to worry about whether or not the meals get cooked!

Last month we spoke about how to find good, inexpensive help (imported from South America, Puerto Rico, or France as well as right in your own back yard). This month I want to deal with the critics mentioned above, by posing a few imaginary situations and giving what I consider to be the correct reply in each case. Notice carefully the answer that you should give:

Situation A

IMAGINARY CHALLENGER: I don't see how you can sleep at night knowing you're exploiting another human being.

YOU: Exploit? Me exploit *her?* The other way around is more like it! She saves up all her phone calls and makes them when I'm out having the poodle shampooed.

47

Situation B

YOU: After all, I pay her $70 a month and give her all the ham hocks she can eat—as well as her choice of any of my old clothes.

CHALLENGER: It's demeaning, dead-end work with absolutely no chance of advancing to anything better. How would you like to change places with her?

YOU: I wouldn't, because I'm *me*. But some people are just cut out for that sort of thing. Sarah Jean adores scrubbing the downstairs toilet. She really goes wild over that downstairs toilet! It's her Thing, just as painting pretty pictures is my Thing. You want I should deprive Sarah Jean of doing her Thing?

Situation C

CHALLENGER: So you pay Lucy two and a quarter an hour, huh? That's really big of you.

YOU: Well, it may not be the highest wage in town, but think how much worse off she'd be if she didn't have a job here.

CHALLENGER: You know she wants to take courses at the college. Why don't you give her an interest-free loan so she can do that?

YOU: Oh, God forbid. She'd get her degree and go off someplace. You know how hard it is to get good help these days.

CHALLENGER: I give up.

And so will your critics! Just remember the important

main points and you will do fine. And be here again next
month as I discuss "Five Points to Look for in Buying
Your Maid a Mop."

Memorable Letters to
Ivory B. Lusterthump

Ivory B. Lusterthump, Th.B., Ph.D., is our consultant for our readers' personal questions about race. We selected her not only because of her ecclesiastical connections (she is a thorough-going middle-of-the-road orthodox Christian and chairman of the Women's Prayer Teas at Big Leather Bible Church) but because of her academic qualifications, which intimidate challengers and reinforce friends. Many readers report that their statements on race are weighted with authority when they add, "It is not just *my opinion*—Ivory B. Lusterthump says so too!" Her first scholarly success, "Specious Reasoning in the *Letter from Birmingham Jail*," brought wide acclaim. It was quickly followed by a faultless monograph entitled "Instances of Genetic Superiority Among Members of the Chicago Police Force." Still causing lively debate in important quarters is her recent study series for church classes, "The Race Question: Let's Not Go Overboard."

Collected here are several letters to Dr. Lusterthump, together with her answers. The editors consider them of lasting value, calling attention as they do to the delicacy

50

and tact with which Dr. Lusterthump answers "the little man's" questions on the personal side of race.

Dear Dr. Lusterthump,

I am an honest person, and when a friend of mine asked me why I don't like black people, I told her right out I don't mind black people—I just don't want to be near them. The reason I don't want to be near them (I am an honest person) is because they have funny hair—and white palms on their brown hands. Also, some of them talk different and act different from me. (My mother first pointed this out to me when I was two, so I have known they were funny-looking and different for a long time.)

Now, my friend who asked the question said to me, "But Flora," she said, "you couldn't wait to visit Europe just because the people there *are* different—with different features, customs, traditions, and all. How do you account for that?"

Well I didn't know how to answer her. What she says is true—I just love Italians, for instance, especially when they are in Italy, and I would go there every summer if I could. How *do* I account for that?

Sincerely,

Flight-Bag Flora

Dear Bag,

The answer is simple. You like Europe because it is quaint and cultural. Traveling there is a different and

51

challenging experience, whereby you tend to become
more educated and more refined. To cite one of my
quotable quotes, "There is a difference in differences!"
It is acceptable to travel 5,000 miles in order to visit St.
Mark's Cathedral and perhaps converse with a typical
Italian there because so many people have done it.
Also, you can take beautiful slide pictures of the
Square to educate yourself and your friends. But my
dear: let your presumptuous friend pause and consider:
If you live in a *normal* neighborhood, which I presume
you do, you would have to go to all kinds of trouble to
meet black people. And what could you possibly learn
from them? The history of Harriet Tubman? *That* isn't
very refined. Besides, I see no possibilities for picture-
taking whatever.

Dear Ivory Lusterthump,

I raised my daughter (who is now twenty-four) in
the church to be a good girl. She was always taught
not to drink, smoke, or say "damn," and to love Jesus.

52

She still does not drink, smoke, or say "damn," and she tells me she still loves Jesus, but she is going with this colored fellow. She says she loves him too, and she's going to marry him. What can I do about it? Answer quickly. The wedding is next Thursday.

Brokenhearted Momma

Dear Broken,

It is a shame that your daughter is twenty-four because if she were under age you could really put the screws on. She is definitely showing signs of belated adolescent rebellion, which may be compounded with serious psychological maladjustments. Be assured that she does not "love" this fellow but is using her relationship with him to display a parental death wish. The best you can do is to keep subtly implying to her that she is emotionally unstable, unbalanced, and that the marriage is destined to fail.

P.S.: Ask her why, if she loves Jesus, she wants to embarrass Him like this.

Dear Madame Lusterthump,

I am a young man who has just been graduated from one of our best seminaries, where I was indoctrinated in all of the right ways. I am sure you would love me if you knew me. But I have a problem. Recently I took over the teaching of the adult Sunday School class at my church because I was not certain that the teacher they had was sound on the doctrine of premillennial implosive exclusion. I began immediately to concentrate on a lesson series relating to the Deeper Life, since nearly everybody in the class was worldly minded. I am happy to say that I have led most of them through the Red Sea and the Wilderness. They are now midway across the Jordan River with their eyes on Canaan—except for one man who won't shut up. He keeps on talking about relating Christianity to the problems of present-day alienation, the technological society, usury, war, hunger, the sexual morass, Asian flu, the price of hamburger, and racial injustice. He is an awful nuisance. What can I do about him?

Anxious Cleric

Dear Anxious,

Perhaps this man simply isn't mature enough to appreciate typology—though I am extremely mature myself, I sometimes tire of it. As for these people who harp on racial injustice, if you look deep enough, you will probably find colored blood. We had a man in our Sunday School class who tried to relate Christianity to open housing. It turned out that his grandmother was passing for white in Glenview, Illinois. If your man hasn't got colored blood, he probably has sin in his life, and he wants to get your mind off it by talking about something irrelevant. For a slight fee I would be willing to come to your Sunday School disguised as an ordinary visitor and take him on.

By the way, what does he say about alienation? I realize it has nothing to do with the deeper truths of

54

the Bible, but my daughter hasn't spoken to me in six years, and I get curious in spite of myself.

Dear Mrs. Lusterthump,

You will note that I call you "Mrs." It is not by happenstance; any doctorate earned by a woman must of necessity be a watered-down one. My purpose in writing is to tell you that I resist to the uttermost the position you assume . . . *not* your position on race, which seems to be remarkably logical for a woman, but the position of authority to which you have so audaciously clambered. I note that some of the people who write you for advice are men, and I also note that you are an "orthodox Christian." Any honest-to-God orthodox Christian—Catholic or Protestant—respects the injunctions of Bible and Tradition with regard to the duty of women, which is to leave their hats on and keep quiet. And *above* all not to seek authority over the Male.

When I need advice on racial issues, I will ask someone who wears trousers and has a well-developed Adam's apple.

What if the Pope were a woman? What if Billy Graham wore culottes? What if Nixon were named Priscilla? Impossible, you say, but such chaos is ultimately brought about by people like you who do not know their proper station in society. No wonder the colored are stepping out of place!

Ernest X. Manley III

Dear Manley,

If *you* were willing to do *my job,* I would gladly step down! I agree with you completely about the submissive role of women, and I invariably so counsel my female clients, who, to a woman, all conceive of themselves as inferior. But Manley, why do you think there are so many women on the mission field? The answer is age-old. Men, superior though they may be, shirk responsibility.

If I quit my job, the Pope might be a colored man. How would you like that?

You *would* have to ask someone else for advice if you want someone who wears trousers. I would never be so brash as to wear anything but a skirt at least three inches below the knee. But I bet my voice is just as deep as yours.

Dear Ivory,

We sent our boy to school to become a rich lawyer, and he has disgraced us by choosing a career as a public school teacher. I took it upon myself to visit his class last week and found him surrounded by children of varying colors and doubtful intelligence in a dangerous and dirty section of our city. His classroom made me gasp. In place of neat rows of desks, our boy had assembled a motley collection of tables, cushions, painting easels, a carpenter's bench, and a small zoo with a ferocious-looking iguana. (He called it a "nature corner.")

Some of the children were writing highly personal

56

stories about aspects of their neighborhood life which you and I know should never be mentioned. One sloppy-looking boy was chewing gum, and our son the teacher laughed at me when I suggested that he order the pupil to take the gum wad out of his mouth and put it on the end of his nose. In the middle of the morning this son of ours, who might have been trying divorce cases by now, led the children out of the building so that they could paint a mural on the perfectly good gray wall that surrounds the school.

I feel as though you are my friend, Ivory, since I have read your column for the past twelve years. Please tell me where we have gone wrong as parents and what we can do about it. Our son is only twenty-five, and I do feel there is hope for him yet.

Teacher's Mom

Dear Mom,

As an orthodox Christian who eschews divorce, I should rather see your son become an insurance lawyer than a divorce lawyer. There's as much money chasing ambulances, you know. At any rate, you're right. You and your hubby were apparently parental dropouts, and now that the price is to be paid, you come running to me. You don't want to know where you've gone wrong; you want sympathy. But you'll get none here. Why didn't you cut off his college tuition money when you first sensed he might waste his life making anarchy in the ghetto? Why didn't you lock him in his room until he realized that good lawyers can make fifty

57

thou per annum and bad school teachers are lucky if they have two suits and a mortgaged car? Where *were* you when his values were being formed?

I can believe your description of the classroom. Your son is part of a conspiracy against the real aim of education, which is to teach children, especially those whom you tell about, to recite the right answers when called upon, keep quiet the rest of the time, and march in orderly fashion to the Basement, as we called it in our day. If his school has the right kind of administrator, he will be fired soon and you won't have to worry. Otherwise you might begin praying that one of the little ones in his class will draw a knife on him some day soon and cause him to see the light. But you may have awakened too late, Mom. My hope is that other parents will read your letter . . . in time.

P.S.: You may feel as though you are my friend but please refer to me in the future as "Dr. Lusterthump."

Dear Dr.,

Things used to be different. I used to sit in my house down at Segregated Shores and worry about my mortgage, my car payment, and my wife's doctor bills. I would watch *Gunsmoke* to take my mind off my worries, and that was life.

Now life is all confused. The TV sometimes has things about race, poverty, war, and hunger that don't soothe me at all. I feel uncomfortable, as though I should do something about something. That would be o.k. if I figured there was no way I could do anything down here at Segregated Shores, which is the way it's always been until a few months ago. Now the church across the street, after no little dissension among its members, is starting a pre-kindergarten for migrant children who live back off in the fields outside our village. And also the church is starting some sort of person-to-person program involving migrant teen-agers (who are said to carry knives). My wife has volunteered to bake cookies for the kindergarten every other Thursday, though I told her to keep her nose clean. Now they are after me. I'm a weakened man, Dr. Lusterthump. I almost want to say yes. How can I say no?

Afraid of Falling

Dear Sir,

This is the kind of question I love. You have indeed been weakened through no fault of your own, and you deserve help. Here are some ready-made answers that will get rid of your assailants and bring you the comfort you need. Say:

1. "My wife has already volunteered." (Don't forget to take the cookie ingredients off your income tax!)

2. "I feel no psychological need to become a do-gooder." (The project is fine for those who are socially insecure or those who need to sublimate sexual unfulfillment.)

3. "I believe I would be a poor Christian witness if I got mixed up with such an argumentative bunch of people." (Didn't you tell me the church members

fought among themselves before they launched this project?)

4. "Did you hear that seven migrant teen-agers up in Prosperity, New York, raped a white girl?" (When you say *that*, they'll have a second thought or two themselves.)

I also recommend that you involve yourself with four-square American young people at a church that is not questionable. If you were spending your time teaching a course in, say, "Following Christ" to clean-cut church youngsters, there would be no possibility of having extra time to spend with undesirables.

Dear Ivy or Ivory or whatever your name is:

Where do you get off encouraging racism like you do? I keep vowing I will never read your column again (my parents subscribe to the rag that includes your drivel), but every time I go home and see it lying there I just can't resist seeing what ignominy you are perpetrating *this* month. When I saw your letter to Mad-at-Medicaid, however, I couldn't keep still any longer.

Listen, Dr. Whoever-you-are, why can't you realize you're playing right into the hands of the power and money structure? You get angry about the handful of people in families with no breadwinner or income who can't afford medical care without help. But you let their doctors who collect $125,000 a year from them (*your* money, too) get off scot free. You get angry at the people on welfare, who receive less than .01 per cent of your tax money, and don't strain a tonsil about the "381 American Millionaires Who Won't Pay Any Tax This Year."

Don't you realize they *want* blacks and whites to be apart and divided and blaming each other for their problems so these abuses can continue? When will you wake up, instead of condemning the poor and fawning all over the real villains?

Disgusted

Dear Readers:

I have included this to show you that I, too, get crank mail. If he knew *my* doctor, Frederick Finebone (who has finally asked me to call him Freddy!), who is as human as you and I, he wouldn't be so quick to condemn these people out of hand!

Integration Is Not the Issue

The problem of housing is a deep and complex one. No one wants to see anyone living in a disease-plagued, rat-ridden slum, paying a rent that would be unfairly high even if the dwelling were less than a total disaster. On the other hand, not many of us are able to do anything about it, short of inviting them to come and live with us or move in on the same block!

It was not until we received the letter that begins this article, however, that we realized it was time to do something on the subject. We turned it over to our expert on real estate, and it remained for him to put the problem in its proper perspective. Here is his answer.

Dear Editors,

I need some help on the subject of integrated housing and this thing of having to sell to whoever comes along.

Suppose it isn't a matter of personal prejudice or even the fact that all my neighbors might move if someone else sold out, leaving me stranded, but simply the economic consideration that my $35,000 house would only be worth $25,000 or less if I were forced to sell sometime? It's not that I value money over human lives or am not willing to take the consequences for a principle, but: How can I keep from losing $10,000 overnight?

Stumped

The best answer to this question is to make certain the situation never arises. After all, "Stumped's" is not the only neighborhood these people can move into; there are many others, I am sure, that they can be directed to which would be happy to have them. It is a matter, simply, of practicing preventive medicine.

How does one practice this sort of prevention? First, by keeping his eyes and ears open for any hints that this is in the offing.* Second, by taking a firm and unshakable stand whenever any such hints are confirmed. Third, by having a definite plan of action, previously formulated, if you are directly involved.

Suppose, for instance, you are the superintendent or realtor of an apartment building in an area which is designated "open housing" but is still overwhelmingly white? You, of course, sympathize with people who want to live in an attractive apartment in a quiet neighborhood at $125 a month instead of a tenement at $175, but there is actually very little you can do about it. You would gain nothing and could lose your job or rating. You might get in trouble with the building owner. You might start a race war that would hardly be worth one individual apartment. So what *can* you, as a Racial Moderate, do?

* See *Another Playground for Greed Valley,* page 136.

When a Negro comes to see about a vacancy you can:

1. Shake his hand, to show that you aren't squeamish.

2. Cite your own personal feelings of good will and best wishes and say that your best pal during the war was a black man.

3. Tell him, "I, personally, would be happy to see you living here, but:

—Look at this Realtor's Point System * I have to follow.

—My job is pretty shaky here anyway.

—My wife is from Georgia.

—The people in this building are so prejudiced your company would cancel your life insurance policy.

—There are no Negro-type churches around here.

—The neighborhood Doberman Pinscher has a thing about dark people.

—My name has been put up for the local fire department.

—The schools here are segregated.

—It would do more harm than good.

—Our policy is two years' rent in advance, which means that you owe me $3,305.52, not including the charge for services. Cash or check?"

* Realtor's Point System (rated on a scale from 0 to 5):
1. Swarthy
2. Wears flashy clothes
3. Speaks with an accent
4. Drives late-model car
5. Is typically "American" in name, family, friends, etc.
   Note: Any broker selling or renting property to a party with an "undesirable" rating will be made to forfeit his commission to the Property Owners League.

Of course, if they do not accept your reasons you will have to resort to other tactics. But surely they will understand how much it means to you—and will look elsewhere.

What happens when the question involves one of your neighbors selling out to a Negro family? As in the other case, the time to act is *before* it happens, your neighbor being the one that must be convinced. While there is no real formula for this, the following recorded dialogue between Theophilus Agnew, pastor, and R. H. Budd, white activist, may be of some help:

65

REV. AGNEW (*after the amenities and tea*):   You're probably wondering what brought me here.

BUDD: No. I'm not.

REV.:   You mean you don't—

BUDD: I mean I can guess. You're on the farewell party committee. The chairman, probably.

REV.:   Mr. Budd, I'm going to be honest with you. Lay my dominoes on the table, so to speak. Certainly I am all for individual conscience and the right to use it, but I must appeal to you as a Christian gentleman not to. I mean, as a Christian gentleman, please consider very carefully to whom the Lord would have you sell your house.

BUDD: Thank you. I already have. Though I doubt if I'm quite your kind of Christian gentleman.

REV. (*cheerfully*):   Well, maybe not, though I always assured everybody that your bark was worse than— Anyway, I'm *sure* you didn't know that our church, three blocks away, has just borrowed $27,000 to add a new Christian Education wing. Work has begun, in fact. But if you sell to—Negroes and others like that, our investment in Christ's Kingdom will be lost. After all, it doesn't matter to *you* who you sell it to—

BUDD: Oh, but it does. You wouldn't be interested in the challenge of an interracial ministry? Or don't unwhite people have souls to be saved?

REV.:   Of course they do! And to tell the truth, if you won't mouth it around, I wouldn't mind having one or two in my congregation. They make very devout Christians, by and large, although . . . . It's just that I

66

wouldn't want the church taken over by them. Then no one would come!

BUDD: Except—

REV.: You know what I mean. And to tell the truth, I don't think they'd really *want* to come. I think they're much happier with their own kind. Why, the other day when my wife asked our cleaning lady about it, she said, "Oh, no, Miz Agnew, *I* don't want to come to your church. I'd feel out of place there. I'm much happier with mah own kind." That's what she said. *You* know they have their own kind of services, all that yelling and rolling in the aisles—ours is just too formal for them.

BUDD: For all of them?

REV.: I think so. It's a racial trait, a cultural thing.

BUDD: But what about the people who tried to attend your church a year or so ago?

REV.: Oh, them. They were just troublemakers, wanting to see what our reaction would be. A sincere Negro Christian wouldn't have done anything like that. Besides: Since then our Board has gotten together and voted that if one earnest Chinese, Korean, or light-skinned Negro Christian were to come and apply for membership, we probably wouldn't turn him away.

BUDD: What's the problem, then?

REV.: I said *one!* It takes time to educate *any* congregation. Still, we're on the way. Last October we finally convinced our denomination that Christian Brotherhood Week wasn't part of the Social Gospel and had a very nice missionary program. And I personally have

67

helped several people get rid of their racial prejudice. But it's a long slow process.

BUDD: I know a quicker way.

REV.: No! They just won't stand for it! And if you force these people to move out it will only make them bitter. You'll do more harm than good.

BUDD: I'm not forcing *them* to do anything.

REV.: Are you saying that my visit has been just a waste of time?

BUDD: I hope not. But—

REV.: I can see that I have no recourse but to take the matter before the throne of Grace. God understands, whether you do or not.

BUDD: Hmm. Do you think He might be trying to tell you something?

Unbeatable Tactics

*For those who challenge the
connection with Christ of your
Christian educational institution*

Since this is a historical tactic, unless you have been doing what you should have been doing for the past forty years (more or less), you will find it useless. Two examples follow:

Lump Christian College: Has maintained a Colored Folks Sunday School for thirty-three years and regularly bussed a group of white students (with adequate faculty protection) to a dangerous section of town once a week. Has taught the students to teach the Colored Folks about Jesus, with the result that the Colored Folks have, to date, learned 153 Christian choruses (such as "God Has Not Promised Skies Always Blue") and 437 Bible verses (such as "Behold old things are passed away and all things are become new"). They also rejoice that 82,609 Sunday School take-home papers have been taken home by the Colored Folks. These papers have admonished little Colored Folk to trust God's will for their lives, thank Jesus if they have had breakfast, wash their faces, and be on time for the Colored Folks Sunday School.

Mighty Fortress Seminary: Has been evangelizing one ghetto for forty-two years. Groups of students have gone to the ghetto (known familiarly as "Our Little Ghetto") three times a week. They have knocked on the same ghetto doors and passed out the same tract ("Are You Missing Something?") 45,360 times. Credit is thereby earned by each successive group of students for a course called "Personal Encounter."

Provided that you qualify, like Lump Christian College and Mighty Fortress Seminary, answer challengers in the following fashion:

YOUNG CHALLENGER: How can you call yourselves Christian at this place? Your buildings are a stone's throw from one of the worst examples of American injustice, and you don't do a thing about it.

YOU: My friend, you must look at the record. Our institution has had an unbroken tradition of concern and involvement with racial problems.

CHALLENGER: *What?*

YOU: Well, what were you doing about racial injustice twenty years ago? Our institution was right in there with the Colored Folks Sunday School. I bet you didn't even know there *was* a ghetto.

CHALLENGER: Twenty years ago I was two years old.

70

You: I thought so. A Johnny-come-lately and probably Not Grounded in the Faith, besides.

CHALLENGER: But now that I'm old enough to see how things are, I—

You: When you get forty years' experience under your belt like we have, then you can start criticizing! Just go off to the chapel and meditate about that, young man!

"Didja Hear the One About. . . ?"

Here is a wise and witty discourse on how to avoid accusations of prejudice (your own!)

At nearly every gathering nowadays, and sometimes even in the privacy of your own home, you will encounter one of those intense, unpleasantly dogmatic individuals whose sole ambition seems to be to pounce on some innocent observation of yours and show you up as "prejudiced." No matter how much you concede, he will always press for more. If, for instance, you are perfectly willing to let Negroes improve their lot in this country, *he* will be urging you to let one be President.

(He is to be distinguished from the Intellectual Liberal who, on finding someone who has just spent three weeks in the ghetto trying to stop the grocery-price racket, informs him how gauche and *wrong* it was, since black people no longer want white interference on any level. In instances like this, the Liberal appears closer to our side.) No, this man is dedicated to the proposition of racial equality and does not attack unless he hears something he interprets as "racist."

Of course, if you are in a situation where you are surrounded by other Clear-thinking Moderates, you may
wish to have a little fun with him. But for now our discussion will be limited to five ways you can end an
accusatory conversation about your "prejudice."

1. JOKE-TELLING *

Tell a joke to muddy the waters

You: Didja hear the one about the little Negro boy who
wanted to be white?

Opposition: No. I—

You: Anyway, he went and put white paint on his face,
then went back into the room and said, "Look, Ma, I'm
white!" and she yelled at him to go wash it off. And
he went in to his daddy and said,"Look, Pa, I'm white!"
and his father knocked him across the room. So he went
out on the front porch and sat down and said, "Boy,
I've only been white five minutes and already I hate
the niggers."

While your opponent is trying to sort out the racist
implications of this joke, you will have ample time to
change the subject:

* Permissible jokes to tell or laugh at:
A. Always—Simple black "wisdom" or misinterpretation in
Southern Negro dialect.
B. Sometimes—Bill Cosby, Dick Gregory, etc., after determining
that content is not anti-white and offensive.
C. Never—Variations of the joke in which a man dies, goes to
Heaven, and somehow returns. When people ask him what God
is like, he replies, "Well, She's black and—"

Tell a joke to gain the offensive

YOU: No, I don't know anything about the housing quota, but has anyone heard the one about the Negro body that turned up in chains in a river down South?

OPP.: No.

YOU: Well, as the people who lived round there said, "Ain't that just like a nigger? Steal all that chain and then try to swim across the river with it!"

By then everybody will be laughing, even though they may think they shouldn't, and any protests by your opponent will only make him seem like a wet blanket. To reinforce this you may say,

"Ah, don't be such a wet blanket."

74

2. THE BACKWARD COMPLIMENT APPROACH

When any conversation is getting out of hand, choose one of the following:

A. "The most Christian man I ever met was Ole Joe, the street cleaner in our town when I was growing up. Black as the ace of spades, but how that man could pray! I tell you, won't be any of us fit to sweep his walk in Heaven."

B. "You can say what you like, those people can really sing!"

C. "If I *knew* they'd be like Aunt Mamie and Ole Joe, I certainly wouldn't mind having Negroes live next door. Why, they'd make a lot better neighbors than most of the white folks I know!"

3. YOU ARE FANATICAL AND

NITPICKING, SIRRAH!

Here again, take your stance quickly as the Clear-thinking Racial Moderate, nonprejudiced but sensible, with the implication that your opponent is fanatical and nitpicking on the subject. Here are three things to say:

A. *On Our Slavery Past*—"Well, after all, we can't flagellate ourselves with guilt about it now, as if we were the only country in the world that ever had slavery. Some countries were much worse; in Russia they starved out villages and made slaves of their own people!"

B. *On Our Present Inequality*—"Well, I think it's time we stopped constantly knocking our country for everything under the sun. It has its faults, sure; I know it's not perfect; but compared to the alternatives I think it's pretty darn good! And I'm tired of hearing it knocked by a few draft-dodgers and hippies!"

C. *On Our Blissful Future*—"These things have a way of working themselves out. If you try to force people into artificial situations with each other it won't help anything; it will only make things worse. White people will resent it. No; these things take time and have to be worked out naturally."

4. WELL, THAT'S NOT PREJUDICE . . .

OPPONENT: Do you realize there's not one neighborhood in this city where a black family can buy a decent home at a fair price? Not one! And in this neighborhood they're barred altogether.

YOU: I know; it's too bad, really.

OPP.: It's a little more than "too bad." And yet you sit there and try to tell me there's no prejudice around here!

YOU: Yes, but that's not prejudice. It's just
(*choose one*)

> —fear of the unknown
> —not wanting to lose money invested in real estate
> —a preference for one's own class of people
> —common sense

Somehow none of these reasons sound quite as bad.

5. TURNING THE SCREWS

When all else fails, there is still one more way of taking the offensive. It is by using what are known as "Moment of Truth" statements, imaginary situations that are designed to reveal the hidden prejudice in your opponent's heart (which he may not even know is there). Simply memorize several, then pose one you consider appropriate. Remember that it is the split-second reaction you want and not the rationalization and intellectual decision that come tumbling after.

As the Moment of Truth takes effect, say quietly, "See? Everyone is 'prejudiced,' so why worry about it?" and walk moderately away.

Eight Moment of Truth Situations

A. It is your first day on a new job. You enter the office eagerly to meet your co-workers and find that your immediate supervisor, the person who will be overseeing and judging your work, is a middle-aged Negro woman.

B. There are two planes flying to California from New York, one carrying a load of predominantly white passengers, one black. Suddenly you learn that a bomb has been placed on one of the two—and that you only have time to contact one of them to warn them to look for it before it goes off.

C. You receive a letter from the school board saying that your child has been selected, pending your approval, to be bussed to a neighboring school a mile away. The class will be approximately 50 per cent black, 50 per cent white.

77

D. You are reading about a fire in which three children died and you are horrified—until you realize from the address that they were slum children from a large family, probably Puerto Rican or black.

E. You are canvassing a low-income area, looking for people who may need additional assistance. You are shown into one home and notice how clean and beautifully decorated it is.

F. You have had a black friend from school with whom you have always gotten along well. You call her up to invite her for dinner and find that she has plans to go somewhere with a black friend—with whom she would honestly rather be.

G. You sign up eagerly for a program to have two inner-city children spend a week in your home—then find out that it is part of the program to have your children go and spend a week in theirs.

H. While at work one day you decide to open a savings account. Walking outside your office, you pass a bank where all the personnel seem to be black. The white bank is four blocks farther.

Who can tell? By this time your critic may be protesting, "But that's not *prejudice,* that's

　　　—a preference for one's own kind of people

　　　—a natural reaction

　　　—common sense

　　　　　too!

From time to time it is the policy of the magazine to print the texts of important lectures or programs on the race question so that readers may have the opportunity of carefully studying the personalities and issues involved. Thousands of readers wrote to thank us for—

The Stapelton Hogsworth–Reginald Raven Interview

As a special service we are printing a landmark dialogue that took place on the popular afternoon television talk program, *The Harry Parry Happy Hour*. The conversation deserves to be studied by responsible Moderates everywhere. Not only does it point up the irrationality and dangerousness of any Negro activist, it also shows how such a person can be dealt with in a civilized fashion in public places (such as the television studio, the platform of the community auditorium, or the married couples' monthly panel program).

On hand as guest moderator for the television show

was Stapelton Hogsworth, the smoothly aged star of such epics as "Genesis and the Gladiators." Once a high school dropout from Smoke, New Jersey, he is currently an eager purveyor of red, white, and blue culture, proponent of a sensible and moral life style, and lover of White House teas. The guest moderator began his interview with controversial Reginald Raven in a laudably moderate fashion:

STAPELTON: And now I want to introduce our first guest.

As you steady viewers all know, your regular moderator, Harry Parry, introduces all kinds of people on this program. He believes—as indeed do I—that all kinds of people have a right to be heard, and that you out there ought to hear all kinds of people. Our guest today, ladies and gentlemen, is none other than Reginald Raven, *the frightening, militant, black-power man.* Please welcome him. (*Leads audience in weak clap.*) How are you today, Reginald?

REGINALD: I'm fine. How're you?

STAPELTON: Putting me on the spot already, eh? Ha ha. Reginald, tell us, how did you get to be a frightening militant black-power man? I mean—outside of the Afro you wear—you look like a decent chap. Why is it you want to make trouble for America?

REGINALD: I should like, if you will, Mr. Hogsworth—

STAPELTON: Please! Call me Stapelton!

REGINALD: Stapelton. That's not your real name, is it? Anyway, as I was saying, I should like to keep America *from* trouble. A great part of my role in the past has been warning America what the country may expect from her oppressed peoples if conditions are not changed. Way back before Watts, I said—

STAPELTON: Is it true that you've been supplying guns to the people on One Hundred and Twenty-third Street? Don't let me interrupt you, Reginald.

REGINALD: I'll try not to. You introduced me as a militant. Just let me say that I'm a militant insofar as I believe the time has come for blacks to stand up for rights that are long overdue, as in the case of—

STAPELTON: Now I don't want to interrupt, Reginald.

82

83

But you can't seriously think that all Negroes are ready for the kind of thing you talk about. That is, you seem to imply that just because a man is black, he ought to be President.

REGINALD: I was trying to say—

STAPELTON: And I think I sense the feeling of the audience here when I say we've been afraid to call a spade a spade long enough for fear of being called prejudiced. I, for one, will go on record as being against—I say against—black violence. You people haven't done yourselves any good these last months, you know.

REGINALD: Are you on record as being against two hundred years of white violence?

STAPELTON: What say?

REGINALD: I said WHITE VIOLENCE.

STAPELTON: Are you trying to give us an example of your black power, Reginald? Ha ha. Ha?

REGINALD: I'd like to talk about black-power things like college admissions, jobs, political office, business capital—

STAPELTON: Political office? I thought we covered that. But don't let me interrupt you, Reginald.

REGINALD: I wish you'd call me "Mr. Raven."

STAPELTON: It's nearly time for a station break, but before that—Ladies, have you tried Climpol's New Blonde-and-Glow? It is true, as my lovely wife can tell you—blondes do have more—(*BREAK and return*)

STAPELTON: Here we are back again with our guest, *Reginald Raven, the frightening, violent, black-power man.* Reginald, we want you to know that we honestly appreciate hearing your opinions. Don't we, audience?

84

I, for one, rarely have the chance to sit down and talk man-to-man with a man like you. In fact, one reason that I enjoy hosting this program is because I get to meet all sorts of fringe people, so to speak. Last time Harry Parry had me, he'd scheduled one of those draft dodgers—that was quite an experience, too. I made the statement then and I stand by it now: if there's any kind of a war when my grandson grows up, that grandson of mine will go to war and fight for America! *How about your grandson, audience?* (*Scattered clapping.*) Now, Reginald, you were telling us why it is that you want to make trouble for America when—outside of that Afro you wear—you look like a perfectly decent chap.

REGINALD: I thought I was talking about black power. To me, black power means that a black man gets paid adequately for doing an adequate job. It means that his son has a chance to go to a decent school—

STAPELTON: I wouldn't interrupt you for the world, Reginald, but what I've always wanted to ask one of you is how can a peace-loving happy people suddenly go crazy for power? Do you know my wife is afraid to go to her evening horticulture class since she read *Look Out, Whitey, Black Power's Gonna Get Your Mama?*

REGINALD: Do you know that our women have been afraid, with a lot more reason, to—

STAPELTON: I hate to interrupt, Reginald, but I think your basic weakness stems back to a certain cultural lack. You tend to react emotionally to anything I say. You people are trying to make judgments on the basis of emotion rather than considered knowledge.

85

REGINALD: What I'd like to say is—

STAPELTON: Please go on. We're really interested in what you have to say, Reginald.

REGINALD: What I have to say is that blacks are tired of being teased with democracy. What we're fighting for is—

STAPELTON: Now you're as much as admitting you want to burn this country down, aren't you, Reginald? Tired of peace? Tired of sense? I want to be kind, and I want to know what you think, but—

REGINALD: Personally I don't want to burn anything down; I want to build something up. But if I wanted to, I couldn't do half the job at burning you fellows have done—

STAPELTON: You're generalizing, Reginald. You're putting me—and this good audience here—in a class with what you call "you fellows." Now I've never had a thing to do with the Ku Klux Klan or anything like that. You shouldn't generalize, Reginald. Please go on, though. We're very interested.

REGINALD: May I simply work a word in edgewise to say that—

STAPELTON: Wait a sec, Reg. The director is trying to tell me something. What's that? Oh, yes! Reginald, we're going to pause in our discussion right now for a little change of pace. . . . (*Background music rises.*) . . . And a welcome one it is too, putting as it does these serious social problems in a better perspective. By way of introducing our next guests, let me tell you something: Yesterday I found out that an estimated 5,280 teen-agers—*both* black and white—in my own

California community have mixed up morals and loose values. But here's a look at the other side of the coin:

Ladies and gentlemen, I'm talking about the All-American Back-to-Bobby-Socks Clean-Cut Youth Chorale. These kids have been circling America, upholding everything decent, from the institutional church to the Federal Reserve System. They're kids who'd *never* call a policeman a bad name or want to take what doesn't belong to them. And nobody'd be scared to meet any of *them* in the dark. Many of us grown-ups, some of us sitting right here, can learn a lot from—The All-American Back-to-Bobby-Socks Clean-Cut Youth Chorale! (*Claps enthusiastically.*)

(*Aside to Reginald*): Their crew cuts are quite a con-

trast to your hairdo, eh, Reginald? Heh, heh.

(*The Chorale sings two stirring numbers, "God Bless Our Native Banks" and "Law and Order Forever."*)

STAPELTON: Wasn't that really great, folks? Now back to our guest, *the angry, frightening, militant, black-power man,* Reginald Raven. Reginald, you were going to tell us why it is you want to make trouble for America when—outside of that Afro you're wearing—you look like a perfectly decent chap. . . .

Social-Action Programs, Right—and Wrong

Last year when we ran an article on the dangers of social-action programs, we were flooded by questions from readers as to whether there wasn't some good type of program by which they could save face, if nothing else. We scouted around and, sure enough, found one headed up by Dr. Respectedwasp, the noted physician. In a subsequent issue we asked him to describe in his own words the kind of social-action program in which he is involved.

Here, then, are both articles.

"BUDDY, CAN YOU GIVE A DAMN?"

"Alms for the poor! Alms for the . . ." "Just one afternoon a week can help a slum child learn to . . ." "Oh, yes, any old clothes you have would be greatly . . ." "Get into the ghetto and . . . give a damn!"

Sound familiar?

Even if it doesn't, don't go away yet. Because sooner or later you too will be confronted by the Social-Action Program (known in our quarters as SAP). And before you know it, if you don't watch out, they will have signed you up!

89

How can you avoid being a sop for SAP? By learning how to identify such programs. In general:

—They involve some skill that looks deceptively simple—and actually is (making a playground from a vacant lot, tutoring a black child, etc.).

—A whole group of people are engaged in it, doing more or less the same thing.

—Someone will want something from you for nothing.

—It (the SAP program) will take up valuable time that could be spent on almost anything else.

—Its underlying philosophy is to involve you firsthand with a type of people you would not otherwise meet; and, once you are involved, it tends to make you fanatical on their behalf too.

—It is a plot to further the cause of the enemy!

Below I have noted a few of these programs you may be asked to help, lifted directly from one of the SAP handbooks. And I have included a very good reason you can give for nonparticipation in each.

1. Set up an inner-city Free Store to distribute clothing, household goods, furniture, toys, etc., collected from the affluent people in your area. You can also stock it with food in dented cans that the supermarkets can't sell and will generally donate. Make it a cheerful place by putting up posters or painting on the walls. Play area music. And make sure, in atmosphere, it's truly "free."

Answer: I am a firm believer in the removal and preservation of all zippers, buttons, snaps, and hooks before discarding garments. I use the fabric for dustcloths. And, frankly, I don't think Those People have the initiative to

make something of what's left.

Or: No one ever gave me anything and I'm better off for it!

2. Start a Save-the-Kids Program in which you go into a deprived area several times a month and take the children you find to the circus, art museum, zoo, or home with you. Try to be with the same children more than once and really get to know each one individually. Then see what else you can do.

Answer: Taking children out of their environment like that will only give them a taste for another kind of life . . . and make them dissatisfied for life in the ghetto as adults.

3. Investigate the Going-to-Court Program (free book-

let on request) which started in Illinois when white suburban women went into the ghetto and stood up in court with children who had been arrested, often violently, for doing nothing more than walking down the street. Justice showed up more often when a Gold Coast executive's wife or other responsible adult stood at the "defendant's" side. And the newly enlightened women went home and gave their husbands an earful about some of the abuses that had been occurring. See if such a program is needed in your area.

Answer: A program like this only perpetuates the myth of police brutality and lack of legal justice for the poor.

Or: Meddling suburban housewives should stay home where they belong.

4. Plan a Teen Center for all races, working with both black and white leaders who have the skill and know-how to relate to kids that age. Have ample recreation facilities and realistic vocational and other information. Consider a scholarship fund, making sure that poor but non-gang kids don't get lost in the shuffle.

Answer: If they're going to be so fussy about who can "relate" to teen-agers (of all people!), why should I even consider it? Imagine being informed that you are inadequate to be friendly with some Black Leopard!

5. Poll the people in a slum area to see what kind of merchant abuses exist (such as giving credit, then doubling prices when the welfare checks come; putting abusive carrying charges on merchandise bought "on time"; delivering an item inferior to the one selected and paid for in the store, then refusing to take it back, and so on).

Explain to the offending merchants that you will boycott them if these abuses are not corrected and then, if they are still unwilling to cooperate, plan shopping expeditions to fair-price stores and supermarkets outside the ghetto. Keep it up until fair practices begin and are maintained in the neighborhood.

Answer: This goes against our whole tradition of capitalism and free enterprise. If these people can't read the fine print or do simple arithmetic, why should the enterprising merchant be penalized?

6. See about setting up a nonprofit day care center so that the neighborhood mothers can shop, work, take job preparation, or go back to school and the children can have some time in an intellectually stimulating environment, guaranteed at least one hot meal a day. Hire a full-time director and dietician but staff it with volunteers and college students who want experience with children.

Answer: Why encourage mother delinquency? These mothers should learn to enjoy their children while they're young.

Or: At the prices I'm paying to keep mine in nursery school, I should waste time looking after someone else's?

In general, once again, avoid anything that smacks of being a *cause* (except of course in tried-and-true areas such as anti-Sex Education or Keeping Christ in Christmas). Avoid the plight of grape pickers, welfare mothers, underachieving Negro children, and all poverty programs.

In short: don't be a sop for SAP!

93

A RACIAL-POVERTY PROGRAM THAT *WORKS!*

"I'm moderate but I'm modern, and I like to be in the swing of things. Is there any way I can 'do my part,' as they say, by participating in a poverty program or a racial-equality project that is neither silly nor dangerous?"

This is one of many similar queries found in our reader mail. In response, members of our staff, tape recorder in hand, visited the home of Dr. Frank Respectedwasp, who is chairman of one of the best racial-poverty programs in the country—one which most of our readers would be proud to duplicate.

Respectedwasp, as a representative of All Saints–No Sinners Church in Pretty Park, Long Island, was selected by the Pretty Park Service Committee to organize a racial-poverty commission for the town. He came well qualified to the post, known to the welfare poor and the middle-class poor alike for his remarkable achievements. He was the first doctor to suggest the $1,000 obstetrical fee as the goal for the public-spirited Pretty Park Doctors' Group, to the acclaim of both his Christian and Jewish colleagues. He pioneered in the $15 two-minute blood pressure reading for hypertensives and in the $12 measles shot for youngsters. Last year he was feted by the Medical Brothers Service and Fun Club for being second in the state to pass the $100,000 mark in Medicaid Payments received.

As we sat in the doctor's charming fifty-foot living room, whose windows overlook a landscaped pool, we were a little awed by the magnanimity of this man in being concerned for a slovenly neighborhood where the

94

people have no such sense of refinement. We turned on the tape recorder, eager to hear about the formation of the commission that would aid them.

Dr. Respectedwasp Speaks

"First of all I might say—though I don't quite know why I feel the need to say it—that I am one of the few among my colleagues of like standing to get myself in a mess like this. I mean, sitting on a racial-poverty commission can be sticky. It's because I'm a Christian that I got into it, I guess. I represent my church on the Pretty Park Service Committee, and when the Service Committee decided to form a racial commission, they wanted to pick someone to head it who was successful but religious, if you know what I mean.

"I would like to tell others how to organize a racial-poverty program, using my own experience as the example.

"*Rule # 1:* Round up the movers and shakers of your community who are really concerned about poverty and racism, and don't be parochial about it. Choose some members who are not Anglo-Saxon, but make sure you don't get any nuts.

"*How I Did It:* I phoned up Jake Fist, a vice president of Consolidated Cyanide; George Stock, the banker; Sam Schlotsman over at International Ladiesware; Timmy Fusion, the Methodist physicist; Dora Geezle, a famous children's author who lives here in Pretty Park (to add a little pizazz); Furtzwig Bunnel, the social theoretician; and Father Latinbacker—he just came out here and I wanted him to feel welcome.

"These were all people who had a certain amount of prestige, and I reasoned that nobody could turn a deaf ear to the results they would turn up. Somebody said I ought to have asked a Mrs. Minny Bates and a Mr. Johnny Vega. Mrs. Bates turned out to be an uneducated assistant cook who lives in the Blacktown section of Pretty Park, and Vega is some sort of artist who started his own half-witted street program with the slum children. Besides, Stock told me he's a Puerto Rican. It was an entirely irrational suggestion.

"*Rule # 2:* Decide on a time and place of meeting.

"*How I Did It:* It was some job, I tell you. We are all people who have busy schedules and appointments to keep. Besides that *I* was, at the same time, chairman of the All Saints Committee for an All-Gold Altar Cross.

"We finally decided on the dinner hour, since we all eat anyway—heh, heh. But that led to another problem. None of us are people who eat just *any place*. I opted for my club, and that would have settled it had not Schlotsman reminded me that the Club has certain opinions about names like Schlotsman. Fusion is used to physicists' conferences, and he wanted to go all the way to the New York Hilton, which I felt was a foolish waste of community funds. Bunnel nearly left the project when he found out we weren't going to Gernley's Gourmet-by-the-Sea. In the end we managed to get by with plain lobster at Dan Dandy's Society Square Restaurant. The wine was a little sharp for my taste, and nobody but a crass industrialist like Fist would have ordered *marrons glacés* for an appetizer.

"*Rule # 3:* Select a title for the racial-poverty program.

"*How I Did It:* I decided before we got to Dan's that our name should be "Project Poverty." Furtzwig was the only one who gave me trouble. Furtzwig Bunnel, the social-theory man, you remember. He wanted our name to be *The Commission to Formulate a Projection of Possible Soft Areas in the Racism-Produced Syndrome of Welfare-Poverty Pockets.*" Everybody else voted him down, to my relief, and "Project Poverty" stuck. It was a catchy name the newspapers seemed to like, with the result that I and my commission were soon mentioned several times in the pages of the *Pretty Park Press.*

"*Rule # 4:* Build a group dynamic through free dialogue and proceed to the issue.

"*How I Did It:* It stands to reason that you can't just leap in and say, 'Well, what shall we do about the impoverished blacks in our town?' Using the skill I have developed at AMA banquets and church board meetings, I subtly set about 'breaking the ice.' Luckily for your

97

readers, I recorded our first meeting on my own Phono-silvercircle Automatic Tape Recorder. Would you like to hear how I built a group dynamic?"

Sitting in Dr. Respectedwasp's charming fifty-foot living room, we quickly nodded yes. We knew that many magazines besiege their readers with tape-recorded interviews, monologues, and dialogues, but we sensed that this article would be the tape-recorded scoop of the month—a tape recording within a tape recording! Dr. Respectedwasp turned on his machine to share with us the first meeting of the racial-poverty commission on that unforgettable night in Dan Dandy's Restaurant. Here it is—just as it happened:

RESPECTEDWASP: This wine is a little sharp for my taste, but I can find no fault with the lobster. How about you, Dora?

DORA: Actually it tortures me at present to eat anything but young soy beans freshly sprouted and honey from the bum-bum flower. I've been convinced that we are what we eat, you know, and I simply adore spending all of the time I'm not writing bookies for the kiddies searching out these fantastic little shops where they sell health foods. Are you interested in health foods, Doctor?

FR. LATINBACKER: I wonder what they eat in the *ghetto?*

FURTZWIG BUNNEL: It just so happens that I personally have supervised seventeen separate studies on the Ghetto Diet.

SCHLOTSMAN: Good thinking on your part, Respectedwasp, to get this man on our committee. In common

98

parlance, "He knows where it's at," ha ha.

FUSION: A fellow in Experimental told me nobody says that anymore.

SCHLOTSMAN: Come now, Dr. Fusion.

RESPECTEDWASP: A-*hem!* And what were the results of your studies, Furtzwig?

BUNNEL: They seem to go for lots of starchy stuff, or, to put it in technical terms—

JAKE FIST: Never mind the technical terms. I say let's cut through the bull and get things moving. That's the way we get things done at Consolidated.

RESPECTEDWASP: Fine idea. Now, I recommend that we choose a subject for tonight's discussion with the idea of forming race-and-poverty goals which will appeal to the community at large. And the people we know in particular.

GEORGE STOCK: What do the blacks want anyway? It's impossible to talk with them about anything. I suppose you all know my brother the mayor. Well, before he was elected, he went to the Blacktown Section to promise 'em a better school, and I tell you the man feared for his life before he got back in our neighborhood. They weren't willing to listen to a thing he promised!

FIST: Did they listen when he promised them a school during the election before last?

STOCK: Well, he didn't have to run for his life, at least.

FIST: Think what would happen if ignorant people like that were in the majority here in Pretty Park!

DORA: The most difficult thing is finding genuine peanut butter. That gop they put in the supermarkets isn't *real* peanut butter at all, you know.

BUNNEL: Out of the processes of limited acculturation which I have watched with interest taking place here tonight, I believe I have discovered the prevailing trend which will lead to a common ground for discussion and the possible formulation of goals.

FIST: How's that again?

FUSION: He thinks he knows what we can talk about.

BUNNEL: The clue came when Stock here said, *What do the blacks want?* Do you follow me?

FIST: My question exactly. What do the blacks *want*, for God's sake?

SCHLOTSMAN: Well, what *do* blacks want?

STOCK: Look at it another way, Gentlemen. What do *blacks* want?

RESPECTEDWASP: Then again, we might say there are blacks and blacks. I offer for your consideration the question, What do *the* blacks want?

FIST: I just dropped my lobster fork. Hey, girl! You! Get me a lobster fork!

LATINBACKER: There's a hothead lady in my parish who says that if we're going to have a racial program we ought to take the program over there to the Blacktown neighborhood.

RESPECTEDWASP: What does she mean by that?

LATINBACKER: She says we ought to go talk right to a mother on welfare and see why that mother's upset about welfare cuts—things like that.

FIST: You know what would happen if we went over there and started asking about welfare cuts. They'd probably expect a handout from *us*.

100

Stock: That's the least of it. Remember what happened to my brother. It's not safe on their streets.

Fusion: I don't know. The firsthand business appeals to me. I'm rather fatigued, what with being holed up at a desk full of neutrino theories. Sometimes it seems those fellows out at the cyclotron have all the fun. Besides, some of us scientists are known for being socially progressive. I for one would benefit greatly from being where the action is, so to speak, on one level, as it were.

Dora: I have an absolutely beautiful idea for Dr. Fusion and all the rest of you!

All: What?

Dora: Next time we meet you can come to my house and I'll prepare us a genuine ghetto dinner! We'll sit down to typical poor-people foods—chitlings and chick peas and romantic things like that. We'll really get the *feel* of being poor! Doesn't it sound delightful?

Respectedwasp: I thought you only ate health foods.

Dora: I shall sacrifice for the Cause!

Fist: This here is one reason we don't have any women on the board at Consolidated Cyanide. *All* women are lame brained, just like all—

Stock: Watch it!

Bunnel: As a young sociologist I spent some valuable time in India where I had several opportunities to eat, as you would call it, typical Indian food, prepared by, as you would call them, typical Indians. The most remarkable part of this experience was to witness the washing down of the cook stove with cow dung prior to sunrise. I would say that there is merit in Miss

101

Geezle's idea, *except* that the food ought to be prepared for us by the racially poor *themselves,* if you see what I'm driving at.

DORA: Are you casting aspersions on *my* chick peas, Furtzwig Bunnel? You haven't even tasted them!

STOCK: Cow dung! Indians wash their stoves with cow dung? That's unbelievable!

RESPECTEDWASP: A-*hem! What Do Blacks Want?* is the question of the evening, Gentlemen. And Lady.

FIST: I don't know about you people, but I've got a meeting with Major Bang from the army tomorrow at eight A.M. If I get some shut-eye tonight, Consolidated just may get a contract for making that new nerve gas.

STOCK: That ought to boost the economy around here. Help solve everybody's problems. (*Aside*) Any time you need capital, Fist, just give me a ring. We know who to take risks with and who *not* to at our place. . . .

RESPECTEDWASP: I might—ah—say in conclusion that I believe we have a right to be proud of what we've accomplished on behalf of working toward elimination of poverty, toward understanding and equality among the races. Let me say—

DORA: I just feel so good about doing my part. Don't all of you?

The Gunga Din Awards

Some cherished honorary

degrees of the past

Last June in our feature Gunga Din Awards (*to Moderates who went slightly above and beyond the call of duty*) *we reprinted a number of honorary degrees which had actually been conferred at some time in American History. These recipients not only upheld our tradition of moderation and clear vision but, in some cases, greatly improved on it! We are happy to salute them once more.*

Award I: To Professor Reginald Droop, 1805

Anthropological Pioneer who discovered in 1804 that "the sutures close earlier in the Negro's skull, thereby constricting his brain."

Award II: To Reverend Georgus Miltonion, 1817

Outstanding Theologian who, in addition to discovering that Africans had actually been brought to America as slaves so they could be converted to Christianity, also redefined the Biblical story of Philip and the Ethiopian (Acts 8:27–31) so that "whereas it might *appear* that the Ethiopian was a man of great learning and trust in a position of authority, who could read when many couldn't, we know that the Lord was *really* trying to tell us that Ethiopians (and their descendants) are a simple unlearned people, joyous but childlike, with definite inclinations towards immorality, stupidity, and crime."

Award III: To Thomas Jefferman, 1825

Honest Politician who, though he saw what some might consider the injustices of slavery, decided, "It would be unfair to set them free and turn them loose on a society that has no provision for them. Besides, I can't afford it."

Award IV: To Harold Due, 1841

British Sociologist who discovered that, "since society is held together by the existence of lower and higher orders, slavery makes for the perfect society."

Award V: To Abraham Lincoln, 1867 (Posthumous)

Secret Moderate who in a little-publicized statement assured everyone that "I am not, nor ever have been, in favor of bringing about in any way the social and political equality of the black and white races; nor in favor of making voters or jurors of Negroes nor of qualifying them to hold office nor to marry with white people. And I will say in addition to this that there is a physical difference between the black and white races which I believe will forever forbid the two races living together on terms of social and political equality and, inasmuch as they cannot so live, while they do remain together there must be a position of superior and inferior and I, as much as any other man, am in favor of having the superior position assigned to the white race."

104

Award VI: To Percy Greenville, 1921

Great White Father and kindly Southern aristocrat who, at the height of a flood when 7,500 Negroes were crowded together on the levee at Scottsboro, poorly sheltered and threatened by an epidemic, used his influence to keep them from being taken off by boat to safety at Vicksburg—on the grounds that such a step would endanger Scottsboro's labor supply.

Fortunately, the sun came out.

Award VII: To Mrs. Andrea Roache, 1945

Outstanding Feminine Achiever who, with other women, names unknown, spread a rumor in the forties that black housemaids and cooks belonged to a secret militant organization called the Eleanor Clubs (named for Mrs. Roosevelt) because they were beginning to demand wages instead of being "given" two dollars a week and "something to carry home."

Award VIII: To Pottius Pugh, 1951

Crack Lawyer who discovered in 1949 that slavery was legal after all and should never have been abolished, because property was guaranteed by the Constitution and slaves, after all, had been property. Although he did not alter the course of history, he is to be commended for trying.

Award IX: To the Alabama Black Shirts, 1962

Labor Leaders who coined the expression: "No nigger is entitled to any job any white man wants."

Award X: To Caleb Cabot Oldfamille, 1969

Leading Historian who, on accepting his degree, said

106

of his latest endeavor, "Negro history is too important now to be left to Negro historians (if there are any). I personally have wanted to do the true story of slavery all my life, and it is sheer coincidence that I have waited until now to begin it. I will continue to deny, as poppycock, all charges that I, C. C. Oldfamille, am just trying to jump on the band wagon and make a fast buck. Black power is only a myth; they need us as much as we need them."

College administrators
face the problem of

Applying Color
with Care

Today authorities in higher education are searching for the answer to a gripping question: how best to open the profession of college teacher to Negroes. No enlightened administrator wants to be stuck with the stigma of an all-white faculty, but on the other hand, every reasonable college president wants to make sure that black participation will be effectively limited. A report from the National Association of Moderate Collegiate Administrators cites two excellent ways to respond. The first, they say, is to hire an innocuous Negro with no qualifications whatsoever. The second is to steal from another educational institution a Negro who has already proved himself adaptable and successful. Thus are alert administrators broad-mindedly—and almost unconsciously—eliminating young blacks with potential who, if they were all given jobs, would upset the color ratio.

A *Fictitious Example*

The first ploy can be illustrated by a fictional telephone conversation between the chairman of a faculty-finding committee and his friend. Let us call our chairman "Dr. George Olympus."

Dr. Olympus begins his conversation this way: "Hullo! This is Olympus down at Bland College. Say, we're thinking of starting an Afro-American department down here. A-f-r-o, yes, Afro—for studies about Nigras. Can you get a hold of any Nigra who'd come down here and teach a course in black poetry to start us out? We plan to put the course in as an elective that everybody can take for half credit. How 'bout that nice fellow you introduced me to at the last sectional conference?"

Dr. Olympus' friend answers, "Oh, I don't know, Georgie. That fellow was a vocational school man who came over to the campus to teach a couple of courses in lithography. Lithography's his field, you see. Printing is his game, not writing."

"Well, they're related, aren't they?" responds Olympus. "He seemed like a goodhearted, mild-mannered kind of chap to me."

The friend agrees. "He is that, yes, indeed. But he's no kind of a poet, though he gets off a good limerick now and then. But I mean he doesn't know a blooming thing about poetry, actually."

Chairman Olympus remains firm. "If he writes limericks and has good manners, that sounds fine to me! He's black as the ace of spades, and black is what we need here right now. Stop trouble before it starts, you know what I mean?"

109

The Brass Cross College Case

The true case of Brass Cross College in Puddles, Wisconsin, shows the second method of dealing with the problem of Negro participation in higher education. Brass Cross, a Protestant school, has been integrated for years, as befits its theological stipulation that "God loves all men." They have had as many as 9 Negroes in freshman classes of 140. Until recently, however, the faculty consisted of 57 white Protestants, spiced up with 2 Catholics and 1 atheist who is a vegetarian. Suddenly it came to President Kingsley F. Goose, Jr., during the All-College Race Relations Week, that he could improve racial relations in the school (and do his bit for the country at large) by hiring a Negro Faculty Member.

Now it was Dr. Goose's habit, when something important was at stake, to regard unsolicited applications in somewhat the same way a sensible editor regards unsolicited manuscripts—obviously not worth looking at, or they wouldn't be unsolicited in the first place. What Goose wanted was one (not *more* than one) Negro Faculty Member who had been solicited all over the place.

Before he got on the phone with his "connections," he made this wise list of qualifications the NFM should have:

1. *Must have very superior academic record.* This did not at all seem incongruous with the fact that Brass Cross had on its staff thirteen people with light brown hair who had excelled with B-minus averages.

2. *Must be well-known in his field and preferably should have published several times.* Goose of course recognized

110

that several of his younger white faculty members needed their Brass Cross experience in order to begin building their careers. Indeed, B.C.C. was humble enough to be proud of helping to place younger teachers in larger colleges after their achievements proved them capable.

3. *Must be a superior example of an adherent to the Protestant Tradition in which the college stands.* Helman Twot in Sociology had been sleeping through college chapel services for twenty years, Paul Epburp in the English department had quietly plagiarized the work of some of his clever students, Dr. Lyman Yaddo had a fund of 548 dirty jokes which were not precisely in line with the Brass Cross Protestant Tradition, and Prof. Dolly Wozzle was known to have snuck off campus for Hari Krishna chants. There were about forty other faculty members who were not what Goose would call *faultless* examples of the college's religious foundations, but he thought that everyone should be allowed a foible or two . . . except the NFM.

4. *Must be known to possess an outgoing personality coupled with poise, restraint, diplomacy, assurance, respect (particularly for the administration), and charm (particularly for college publicity stints).* Among fifty-odd white Protestants, one was bound to get some churlish creatures who snarl and slop around a bit. . . . But that's a different proposition altogether.

After Goose had made his list and phoned his connections, he started talking to prospects and was surprised to learn that none of them was anxious to come to open-armed Brass Cross. One fellow was downright rude about it.

"Listen here, I'm *already* integrated. I've established my career; I've got a name, a future, and all the white

112

friends I can stand in three lifetimes."

"That's exactly why we want you," Goose patiently explained. "We need somebody who has proved beyond doubt that he can fit into the Brass Cross picture. Now that it's the thing to do, we're very anxious to have a Negro professor participating in our campus community—"

"If you really want to increase black participation in *America,* why don't you hire somebody who doesn't already have a job? There are plenty of blacks around who are at least as well qualified as anybody on your faculty."

Here Goose lost his patience. "How in God's good name could we take a chance on a man like *that?*" he answered.

Weeks later President Goose finally landed a suitable Negro Faculty Member (who by that time he had learned to call "Black Faculty Member"). In order to land the right man, he had to create and raise money for a Race Relations Grant so that he could offer a famous black professor half again as much as he was already getting at his already successful job.

After conquering his racial problem, Goose found time to dump the pile of unsolicited faculty applications that had been cluttering his desk. Among them were the applications of seven black men and women. Goose had not made a mistake in leaving them unconsidered. Later research in the wastebasket showed that, though the people were qualified, they were neither innocuous enough to fit the Olympus method of handling black participation nor perfect enough to suit the requirements of Brass Cross College.

113

People like our fictional George Olympus and great minds such as Kingsley F. Goose are hard at work seeking—and finding—the answer to the question of Negro participation in the colleges. Encouraging is the fact that, in spite of the growth of shortsighted radical employment practices, sensible men are holding firm to good values. And they are joined by their brothers in many businesses and professions.

Dear Suggestion Box. . .

I am writing, not with a problem but with a suggestion for the reader, M. Sergius, who was disturbed over Creeping Liberalism in the Sunday School.

Our church, Save-Some-Souls Episcopal, has always observed Christian Brotherhood Week (as dictated by some big cheese in the diocese), but this year, instead of a nice program about our Brethren Round the World, with a table of African spears and shrunken heads set up in the narthex, they distributed this material that looked as if it had come from the Communist wing of the U.N.— complete with a motif of children of all different shades dancing around in a circle and holding hands! And the text of this wishy-washy watered-down type of equality preaching was even worse than the silly little pictures accompanying it.

My first reaction of course was to see red, but since I am proud to be known as a Moderate who does nothing rash, rather than make a fuss I simply and quietly adapted the material for the class I teach, giving it the best interpretation possible. I am enclosing a sample of what I did, in case you have other readers who find themselves in the same boat. Reprints of the full lesson are available from me—at a slight charge, of course.

115

SAMPLE LESSON

Interpreting Visual Material
   *(Based on actual questions asked me
   by my class)*

Q: In the picture of that African tribe, why is that boy laughing and wearing nothing but beads and a string?

A: Because we haven't gotten to him with the Gospel yet.

Q: In the picture of the Three Wise Men in Sunday School and on Christmas cards, why is the Negro one always last?

A: Because he was smart enough to know his place. How do you think he got to be a Wise Man in the first place?

Q: Look, Miss Barrel, it says here that if Jesus were around today He'd no doubt be poor and maybe black like in this picture!

A: That's ridiculous. We know from reputable pictures handed down to us that Jesus was fair-skinned with a sweet smile and wavy brown hair to His shoulders. There is no reason to doubt that He would look exactly the same today except that His hair would be cut above His ears and He would be more contemporarily dressed in a suit and attractive tie.

Q: Why do they have all sorts of children, Chinese and Negro and white, all together in this Sunday School class picture?

A: Because they paid the little brats two dollars an hour to *pose* for such a picture.

Q: But it says here—

A: Never mind! That's just to make the picture seem authentic. Now, who knows what authentic means? It's taken from some Greek root, meaning to—

Learning About Other Nationalities

Directions: Match up the following racial characteristics with the nationality you feel best typifies each:

      Orientals   amoral
      Italians   superstitious

117

Negroes	like emotional church services
Jews	musical
Indians	like flashy clothes
	inscrutable
	childlike and fun-loving
	noble and red-skinned
	shrewd businessmen
	untrustworthy
	pushy
	eat funny food
	cold-natured
	easy-going
	slant-eyed and yellow

Showing Brotherhood to Others

Now, boys and girls. Who can think of one way in which we are already showing Brotherhood?

That's right. By our pig bank. Our Jeffrey the Pig bank in which we put our pennies every week so that they can go to help Cleansing Black Diamonds (little African children with scabious diseases). Here, Gladys, why don't you pass Jeffrey for us?

There. Now you all know what Brotherhood means. In closing, let us sing the first verse and chorus of "Brighten the Corner Where You Are."

(*Editor's Note: The full lesson can be ordered from Drawer D, in care of this magazine, for only $.75. Order yours today!*)

Wallis B. Whitelaw, a favorite contributor to the White Trumpet, *illustrates his talent for the warmly human case history in an article for businessmen—*

Believe Your Own

Other Reasons

If a minority group member answers your want ad, and there is nothing for it but to hire him (or her), is it permissible to fire him (or her) within two weeks? This is a question with which small businessmen are, as they confront equal opportunity laws, more and more often faced. Certainly if quality and caliber are to be maintained among us, it is necessary to be continually aware of the need for the consistent practice of a high business ethic. One cannot fire a person in two weeks without a reason, and any ethical businessman would find it shabby to shrug his shoulders and say with an embarrassed giggle, "I'm firing you because you're incompetent," when he does not really believe the individual he had to hire *is* incompetent.

Fortunately there exists an ethical way to get rid of any undesirable employee whom you did not want to hire in the first place; a positive way to answer the question that begins this article. You, Mr. Businessman, must only believe you are *not* firing the employee because he (or she) is the wrong color. You must only believe your own *other* reasons!

The Story of Bayard Mop

One businessman who succeeded is Bayard W. Mop, longtime tenor soloist at All Souls for the Rosary Church and owner of Bayard W. Mop Summer Rental, Inc. Recently, he placed an ad in his diocesan paper, hoping to find a good, competent, Christian secretary. Bayard had two reasons for advertising in the diocesan paper: he thought perhaps that a good Christian secretary might work harder for less money, and, as the inevitably concerned churchman, he thought that after she got to working he might be able to convince her to help with his parish youth group, which was at the time in dire straits.

Black Girl Answers Bayard's Ad

The first girl who answered the ad was unassailably qualified. She had a college degree, a typing speed of 200 correct words per minute, a phenomenal grasp of summer rentals, and spiritual recommendations from three Jesuit priests, fourteen assorted sisters, and one Baptist preacher. In her interview she mentioned that she would just love the opportunity of leading a local parish youth group in her spare time.

But she was coal black. Not brown, mind you, which Bayard might have been able to take after the first shock of it, but black. Her hair was "natural" (you know how *that* looks) and her face was not the familiar television-screen face. She didn't look like a tanned Caucasian at all. She looked like a—Negroid. Bayard Mop had never been so confused in his life. His customers *seemed* to love her, but he knew that they couldn't and he was afraid he would lose all of his business.

She worked a steady week without making one mistake, during which time he assured her that the youth group at All Souls for the Rosary was going great guns and had no need of a new leader after all.

Bayard Faces the Situation

Bayard, as befitting a Christian, was scrupulously fair about matters. Although the secretary had shown no outward signs of incompetence, he reluctantly resigned himself to the fact that this outward behavior was a clever disguise of the truth.

He knew that the truth would show itself sooner or later, but of course he neither hounded her nor hung over her desk as he waited for her first error. Mainly he stayed in his inner office and prayed a lot.

On the tenth day of the girl's employment, Bayard was sitting in his inner office telling himself that he really liked the black girl and would hate to have her leave when he happened to turn the volume all of the way up on the intercom while letting his friendly voice come through it without warning. The result at the receiver on

the secretary's desk was a banshee's scream—the sound of
fair and friendly Bayard amplified several hundred times.

The secretary was typing a letter—a rather important
letter—when the scream came through, and for some reason she jumped. In the process a dark question mark
appeared on the letter in the place where a comma should
have been. (After "yours sincerely," of all places.) Bayard,
running apace at a pant from his inner office to her desk,
saw the darkly printed question mark with his own eyes.

"I'm terribly sorry but this will never do," he told the
secretary as calmly as possible. "It's a good thing I just
happened to come along at the right time so that I caught
your mistake. It could have been disastrous but you probably wouldn't realize that. I'm afraid I've given you a bit
too much responsibility."

"But of course I'm going to erase it, Mr. Mop. I never
would have let you sign it that way." Her ears were

pierced too. He bet anything that after work she wore long African earrings with witch-doctor symbols on them.

Bayard Feels Sorry

"I'm terribly sorry about this, I really am. . . ." He really was, just as he was terribly sorry about the series of her mistakes that followed in the next few days. She was getting the impression, in spite of everything he did to cover up his opinion, that he thought she could do nothing right. "Just relax," he told her on the twelfth day. "I'll give you the whole morning to type out this little bill. Now you just take it one word and one number at a time, and I'm sure you can type up the bill as well as anyone!"

"It's funny," she murmured. "After being with you for twelve days, I can hardly believe I got straight A's in every business course I ever took."

"A real job is never the same as being in school! But I'll help you try to make the grade if you possibly can!"

Bayard Conquers

Even with this kind of encouragement she turned in a bill that was typed a little darkly in some places and a little lightly in others. If one looked at it closely, the result was absolutely jarring. He was increasingly sorry about the situation. He knew that it was possible that the girl had been culturally deprived because of the practice of unequal opportunity abroad in the land. Still, he reasoned, should an employer be expected to put up with a secretary who cannot tell the difference between a ques-

123

tion mark and a comma? Should a person be required to pay a girl who cannot turn out one aesthetically pleasing bill in a whole morning?

With great regret Bayard Mop found that it was necessary to replace his Negro secretary—*not because she was black, but because she was incompetent.* Bayard, however, was entirely competent—which is the point of recounting this moving case history. He thoroughly believed his reason. His story should bring hope to many businessmen who are faced with similarly ticklish ethical problems.

Unbeatable Tactics

DESEGREGATION MADE EASY

Words of praise are in order for the desegregation tactic originated by Bring the Truth Mission, which operates a hospital in Darkest Africa where scores of pagan natives have been shown the love of Christ.

For some thirty years the hospital has separated white patients from native patients, finding the practice to be compatible with the natural order and the will of God. But restless troublemakers have of late agitated for integration of the hospital facilities, calling to question Bring the Truth's version of the Christian gospel.

"We saw their point (though their main object was devilish disruption, of course) and we immediately integrated the hospital," relates Director of Nurses Mrs. Rachel Whitehope.* "However, we are glad to report that there has been no ensuing chaos because desegregation was accompanied by a clever new financial policy:

"Some sections of the hospital were made 'Private,' and patients must pay for these or else be members of the Mission's Purple Cross Hospitalization Plan. (All of our staff members are automatic members—the cost is figured

* No relation to Samuel Whitehope who sat in at the Redneck Beanery.

126

in their support allowances.) Other ward-type facilities were labeled 'Public,' and the fees for these are adjusted to what a typical native is able to afford. A bed in one of our 'Public' wards may cost a sick man a chicken if he can spare one, or it may cost him absolutely nothing if the poor creature is as economically unstable as most of them are. To date we have not had one native in 'Private' nor one white in 'Public,' though all beds are open to everyone.

"We are keeping a one-bed private room available at all times as added forethought. The wife of the President of the country, who is said to be as black as coal, expects to deliver here next month, and she has already prepaid for the 'Private' section, which put us in a flurry at first.

"We heartily suggest our tactic to those who may have similar troubles. The natives are getting restless everywhere, it seems. We take it to be a sign of the end-times."

Button, Button,

Who's Got the Vote?

A sense of fun is a must for a Racial Moderate if he is not to become disheartened, and it is with this in mind that we reprint the following "games." These games, taken from the Registration Handbook of one of our finest states, are played when the opponent (usually Negro) is trying to win the chance to vote and the defense (usually sheriff, registrar, or populace) is trying to keep him from it. We hope they will provide a chuckle.

The titles are, by and large, explanatory, and there is an example given with each.

1. HIDE AND SEEK

Example: Sammy Blackear, who spent thirteen days in his home town of Humane (Pop. 178), trying to find out who the registrar was. One day, by accident, when he was waiting in line to get a haircut, he overheard someone drop a hint that the town beautician was the properly elected official. He rushed down the street to her shop and, sportsmanlike, she admitted it and sent him to her office next door. When the office turned out to be an abandoned outhouse, he hurried back to her beauty

128

parlor and found that the door was locked and bolted. It remained that way until November 5. He lost, of course, but by clever gamesmanship *she* was "home free."

2. GUESS WHO?

Example: Phineas Dodd, great-grandson of the town's founder and pastor of the African Baptist Church. When he went to register, he said, "I would like a registration form, please."

"You live in this precinct?"

"Of course, Miss Lindy. I'm Phineas *Dodd*."

"Who?"

"You know me—we almost went to school together."

"I know who you remind me of. But you'll need two credible registered voters to say who you actually are."

This was the most difficult part of the game (for Phineas) since all of the registered voters were white, but he finally found two who were willing to vouch for him: the postmistress (who was independently wealthy) and the local F.B.I. Man-in-residence (whose salary was paid elsewhere).

"Miss Lindy? Phineas Dodd again. Here are the people to identify me."

"Wa'al, wa'al, wa'al. He's O.K.—I guess—but I'll have to reject her."

"What? Why?"

"She was already in here to identify someone else. You can't come in here but once."

"Oh."

And since Phineas had already asked everyone else in town he decided, wisely, to concede the match. .

3. PATIENCE RELAY

Example: 5,000 registered Negroes in the city of Mole who were sent notices (duly sworn out by two other registered voters) challenging their right to vote. To prevent removal of their names from the roll they had to appeal within ten days—nine of which the Registrar's Office was closed, due to premium fishing weather. On the tenth day, however, the office was open (as a reward for perseverance) from 3:41 P.M. to 4:20 P.M., during which time two Negro voters were able to make an appeal.

It is not known whether they scored a hit or not.

4. OBSTACLE RACE

Example: Mindy Mae Brown, college student and research assistant, who was found to be unable to fill out the simplest registration form without making mistakes. The last time she tried she misspelled two words, miscalculated her age (in months), and failed to fully answer the question, "Give a statement setting forth your understanding of the duties and obligations of citizenship under a constitutional form of government" in the two lines provided.

5. BOMBARDMENT

Example: Waldo Jones, who discovered after he had finally successfully registered that he was unable to buy gas for his car, food for his family, or coal for the furnace. When he got home he found that his telephone had been disconnected. As it turned out, however, it didn't matter because the next night someone burned his house and garage down.

6. RED LIGHT

Example: R. Swampfoot, who has been faithfully playing for fifteen years.

"Hello, Miz Lindy."

131

" 'Lo."

"Uh—last year when that Federal marshal was here and I registered to vote? I was never notified if it were successful or not."

"Well, let's see." Looks through files. "No. It weren't."

"Do you mind telling me what was wrong?"

"Thinking of appealing, are ya?"

"No. I just wanted to know so I wouldn't—"

"Wa'al, I don't know what it was. Couldn't tell you, anyway; it wouldn't be cricket. But you can always try again next year if he comes back. Maybe you *won't* make the same mistake twice."

7. MARATHON RACE

Example: Black voters who had won at the other games and were already registered. Before receiving a ballot they had to write out the Constitution, the Bill of Rights, eighty-nine of the state by-laws, and twenty Great Hymns of the Church. Unfortunately, most of them were still on "Amazing Grace" when their ten minutes were up, though there will always be one or two who make it.

But, make it or not, as in all the games, though they ultimately lost, they had a great time playing.

Best Contest

of the Year

Healthy competition is always enjoyed by our readers, and the magazine has sponsored many contests throughout its history. We were overwhelmed with the response to one of our contests this year, co-sponsored by the magazine and by Athens S. Swinger, a charter subscriber. A representative of the Hemlock Advertising Agency, Mr. Swinger was looking for seven types of Negroes to pose for the advertisements of his assorted clients. The magazine published his requirements and offered prizes to readers who could "Find the Right Negro."

To Mrs. T. Tinckle went the first prize for finding four "just right" Negroes:

—One black male (30–45) with the perfect black-beer-drinker's face. (Seven breweries were in competition to find the man for this job.)

—One clean-cut, tame-haired, innocuous-looking religious-type black (19–22) to pose with fourteen white students for college advertisement to be placed in conservative Christian periodicals.

—One Negro female, nonglamorous but neat, to be shown

133

in Before and After photographs for deodorant ad. Able to express total dejection and failure to relate to a selected integrated group (for the Before photograph) and total assurance and success in social orientation (for the After pic).

—One "real-person"-type Negro female with slightly irregular features and "real"-type smile to be shown making friends with Gunk cigarettes.

Mr. H. Q. Bean brought in two of the needed Negroes, for a well-deserved second prize:

—Two blacks (counting as one for the contest), one male, one female, who look chic but yet are easily identifiable as average black wage earners, to be photographed living the good life right along with their white neighbors in an X-37 Tailzoom automobile which cost them a year's salary.

—One sharp Negro male to project status and acceptability in a waist-suppressing, custom-made Edwardian suit. A trip to a posh beach club in Smarthampton, outside the white gates of which the picture will be taken, is in store for the lucky man Mr. Bean found.

Dr. Layton Snork scored for third prize. He rounded up:

—One professional-type black male with well-groomed mustache to pose with slide rule for the Stars and Stripes Rocket Accoutrement Corporation. The slug line for this advertisement will read: "TO US A MAN IS A MAN: we don't care what color his skin is so long as he has the talent and skill to help us build a ballistic missile with overkill. We are AN EQUAL OPPORTU-

134

NITIES EMPLOYER—and what opportunities we have!"

Prizes included lifetime subscriptions to the magazine, autographed photographs of the editors, and a tour of the Hemlock Advertising Agency. Mrs. Tinckle, first-prize winner, was also invited to lunch on Mr. Swinger's expense account.

Another Playground
for Greed Valley

The story of a town that stumbled on an enchanting but legal way of solving its racial problems

Greed Valley is a stable, middle-class suburb, law-abiding and God-fearing, much like yours or mine—but with a difference. For they have discovered an effective way of keeping un-American-looking and community-threatening people out. Whenever such a threat arises and nothing else works, they simply condemn the land for: (a) a park, (b) a school, or (c) a municipal swimming pool. Besides taxes that might seem alarmingly high to some, recreational facilities in Greed Valley are excellent and include a baseball diamond or swimming pool for every three houses and elementary education on a one-to-one basis.

Background

Since, perversely, this type of threatening situation arises at least once a year, the people of Greed Valley have devised a stable pattern of coping. I use the word

"Coping" because, surprisingly, not all of the people living there favor this homogeneity and gracious living. There is token opposition from a "Human Rights Council" that always steps up like the town drunk to take issue, reeling around and tossing off such comments as "Every study shows that property values remain constant and rise with the normal market as long as neighborhood residents keep their heads" and "This isn't even a decision between conscience and status, between the dignity of man and the tyranny of the dollar. You don't seem to realize you no longer have the choice!"

Response

"They think they got us," drawls Simon Bowinckel, a ruddy, rough-hewn man, a shrewd businessman and head of the Parks Commission. "But they don't got us, not on your mama's pink garter. Those jerks can't understand that integration is *not* the issue and never has been. The issue is municipal rights and the right of the majority to be heard. It is the sacredness of private property and the right to dispose of it as a man sees fit. Our motto is 'Come swim with us in Greed Valley' and 'A teacher for every student,' although once in a while they have to share. But families tend to be small around here, what with the taxes. Still, you'd be surprised what people are willing to pay for the insurance of a stable community."

As soon as Simon Bowinckel learns of a particular situation, he gets to work on the phone.

"Hello, Walter?"

"Speak-ing."

137

"Walter?"

"Yes dear?"

"Oh. You sounded, ha ha, like your secretary, that high—Look, we've got trouble again, if you know what—"

"Surely you jest, Simon! Not *another* government-backed builder."

"No, no, nothing like that exactly. But you remember that sixty-thousand-dollar house being built on the lot across from the cemetery? For the doctor?"

"Yes?"

"Well, it turns out the good doctor's a little browner than we expected."

"No!"

"Uh huh. And it turns out I can't even get a red light for a building specification violation. The shack was approved several months ago, when we thought—"

"You know, it's not the man's color that bothers me; it's the fact that he went about it in such a sneaky way!"

"Yeah, he must have known what would happen if he didn't. He wouldn't have gotten an ordinance through in twenty years! But anyway, I'll do what I can, though it may come to a vote."

"Oh, Simon, not another *school!*"

"No, not with the forty-eight we already have. I was thinking of putting a bandshell there. It'd be a real peaceful view. . . ."

In the meantime, before a public information meeting is held, the house is often vandalized. When this happens, they:

1. Get a stop-work order for dangerous conditions. "I don't know who the builder is, but this is the worst con-

138

struction job I've ever seen!"

2. Realize it must have been the work of juveniles who do not have enough parks to play in.

3. Decide finally that the builders must have staged it themselves in order to gain national sympathy.

Public Information Meeting

This meeting is important because, although only the Town Council and the Parks Committee can vote, this lets them know that they have the full support of the community behind them. The day before the meeting, in fact, a selected "realtor" calls up anyone known to be

139

undecided and offers him a third of what his home is worth "in the event that the park vote doesn't go through."

At the Meeting

At the meeting, ten appointed people rise and say the following litany:

ONE: Since I know you people are the stuff of which *real* Americans are made, I know you'll want to do the best by your kids.

TWO: Integration is not the issue.

THREE: I certainly wouldn't force my way in if someone didn't want me somewhere.

FOUR: I'm not a bigot; I certainly don't go around hating people of other persuasions. I think Chinese, Negroes, or anyone else has the right to decent houses, as good as ours. Just not in Greed Valley!

FIVE: I must oppose it as a Christian because you can't morally compel love; you can't force people to love someone else. Love under compulsion is against the divine scheme of things. Blacks should work toward desirable ends through example and persuasion, uplifted and tempered by love.

SIX: Reverend Biggod is right. Everybody knows that downzoning is the next step!

SEVEN: The people behind this sure couldn't be Christian: They've stirred up hate in my heart toward the niggers that wasn't there before.

EIGHT: Yeah. By forcing this on us they're creating more prejudice than brotherhood!

140

NINE: Integration is *not* the issue.

TEN: I'm certainly not concerned with depriving any member of any minority of living wherever they want; but I've got proof positive that this particular doctor is known to associate with Commies!

ONE: I came here to get away from niggers, not live with them!

TWO: Let one in and he'll open the door to the rest!

THREE: They'll wreck our parks!

FOUR: Attack our daughters!

FIVE: Lower our property values!

SIX: I'm not a bigot but—

SEVEN: The Unitarians are behind this!

EIGHT: The Quakers are behind this!

NINE: The clergy are behind this!

TEN: Black power!

ONE: Green power!

TWO: Park power!

THREE: Vote!

141

The Evils of

Intermarriage

A great many people, both black and white, have said that Negroes couldn't care less about marrying your daughter; that in the face of the struggle for decent housing, well-paying jobs, a good education, and freedom of opportunity and movement the thought of intermarriage is hardly uppermost in their minds. Do not be deceived. Since marriage in this country is still based on the mutual consent of both parties and not on coercion, it must be supposed that there are at least *some* Negroes with unbeatable powers of persuasion running around, ready to convince whatever vulnerable white girl happens to come along that they should be happily wed. And the situation is not improving!

In view of this, we conducted a survey, an impartial poll, to find out the feeling of white America (with one exception) and asked the following questions:

1. Would you like your daughter to marry a Negro?
2. Would you like your daughter to marry a midget? A black dwarf? A garbage collector?

3. Would you like your daughter to marry, period? (Would you like to marry your daughter yourself?)

4. If your daughter were Phyllis Diller, would you let her marry Sidney Poitier?

5. Are you in favor of intermarriage generally? Specifically? Why not?

And so on. What we found was both interesting and significant: a resounding "No!" in most cases to the first four questions and some fascinating answers to number five. So fascinating and reassuring, in fact, that we decided to share some of them with you.

An Ivy League Professor confessed to us: "Civilization is deteriorating fast enough as it is, and absorbing the Negro would only speed it up. Genetic race differences show the Negro to be much lower in abstract ability. He is strong, he has a sense of humor and an amiable disposition, but he simply doesn't have the ability to do arithmetic problems."

From a High Official in the American Nazi Party: "Amalgamation is the ultimate goal of the Commie element and the civil rights movement because it would mongrelize the races until there *was* no black or white. Then the dirty Jews and Mexicans and Polacks would take over!"

A Political Columnist who asked not to be identified told us: "It is a bad racial combination and can only lead to the collapse of both races. No, I don't want to explain that. I concede it is a matter of dispute and that some people can give studies in support of the other position. But I'm not impressed by these studies, that's all. No, I won't explain why. It's my opinion and that's all there is

143

to it."

And this philosophic word from a Writer in Louisiana: "Well, gee, marriages of any kind are hard to make and that kind would be impossible. After all, people don't just marry each other, they kinda marry the world. And my part of the world don't take kindly to that!"

We found also that there were religious aspects to the question. The Dean of a Bible College mentioned to us: "In order to preserve our traditional freedom to enroll all races, we don't permit students to do anything that would call attention to it—including interracial dating. We counsel very strongly against any such involvement and put it to them this way: If you *do* intermarry, you might as well forget about being a Christian. Because as a Christian you'll find your whole sphere of influence among Christians is cut off. Who's going to listen to someone who's done such a terrible thing?"

And a Wealthy Rancher from the Southwest adds: "You're a white man, ain't ya? God made you white and He wants you to stay that way. *He* was the first real segregationist: He put the white man in Europe, the red man in America, and the black man in Africa—all separated by oceans and deserts and mountains. Why didn't He just put them together in the first place if He wanted them to be?

"What do you mean, how did I get *here?* You know as well as I do that if the Indians were too dumb to hang onto what the Good Lord gave them, that ain't *my* fault!"

And, finally, the exception. We quote him not because we necessarily agree with what he says but to show you how a growing number of Negroes feel about the subject.

144

Here are the genuine words of a genuine black militant:

"You'd better believe we're not interested in any of the trash white America has left over to palm off on us. People, all people, have begun to realize that black *is* better, black is more pure, more beautiful, more everything. And this band wagon is already full, so keep your lily-whites off us!"

Naturally, as we said, we don't agree with the gist of his statements but we certainly applaud the spirit behind them!

As we traveled the country, asking questions, there was one question, in turn, that concerned parents asked *us:* "What can I do in my own family situation to prevent this from happening someday; how would I handle it if my daughter were involved?"

And so, based on the helpful comments we received, we have included an imaginary dialogue and a discussion of the subject which show better than mere rhetoric exactly what can be done.

HE'S WHAT?—AN IMAGINARY DIALOGUE

Scene One

YOU (*the father*): He's what?

DAUGHTER: You *do* need a hearing aid. I said, Jeff is—

YOU: Now wait a minute! You said he was a lawyer; Phi Beta Kappa and under contract to write a book!

DAU: So? You were the one that colored him honky.

YOU: Oh, fine. What's this soul brother's name, anyway?

DAU: Well, it was Jefferson Davis Lee. But for obvious

146

reasons he changed it—to Jeff X.

You: And you're going to be Mrs. X.

Dau: I didn't say that! Right now I just wanted to talk to you, see how you felt. Nothing is definite yet.

You: Oh. Well, don't pay too much attention to what I said. You know we only want what's best for you.

Dau: Good. I was hoping you'd say that.

You: Siddown! You'll marry some black buck over my dead body!

Scene Two (*Two hours later*)

You: So he thinks he can support you and that you'll have ten children, half your own and half adopted from racial mixtures (*shudder*) that no one else wants. No doubt ten of them can take care of the discrimination problem. But there *are* still a few little things I'd like to know about.

Dau: What?

You: What do you think the neighbors will think about it?

Dau: Neighbors? What neighbors?

You: *Our* neighbors.

Dau: Oh. Well, we were planning to get married quietly up at school, but I'm thinking now of getting a parade permit and coming down here and—

You: You may think it's all very funny, but *we* have to live here! Wait till you try to find a place to live. I can tell you you'd never be accepted in this neighborhood.

Dau: Well, actually we weren't planning to come and live with you. We were thinking more of an academic community where I could continue to teach.

147

You: They'd let you?

Dau: Oh, come on. I wouldn't be the first!

You: Well, fine. You're looking out for yourselves, I can see, but how about a little concern for your brother?

Dau: My brother? What's wrong with him?

You: Nothing now; but who's going to want to marry *him* and have a Negro brother-in-law?

Dau: Oh, Lord. He's only eleven. A lot can happen in ten years.

You: And the minister! What will the people around the church think of the minister when they see you? You could ruin his career! I presume you *are* having a clergyman marry you?

Dau: Of course. But he's not interested in his "career," as you put it. My minister is interested in—

You: I don't care what he's interested in! Anyone fool enough to consider scrambling up the races like that doesn't deserve my consideration about anything! He— I only hope your great-grandmother in Ireland never finds out. It would *kill* her.

Dau: I won't tell her if you won't. You haven't written her for years.

You: Well, I can't *lie* to her about it.

Dau: You know, I don't think all this talking is getting us anywhere.

You: No. You're right. But promise you won't rush into anything, that you'll think it over carefully. Youthful impetuosity and all that. After all. . . .

Dau: Yes, Dad?

You: You're only thirty-one.

(*Fade out, while she considers this fact thoughtfully.*)

148

Discussion: What Further Can You Do?

1. Talk to your minister, if he is the right kind of minister.

2. See the advice of Ivory Lusterthump in this anthology and, if necessary, write her for more.

3. Keep any further discussion on a higher spiritual plane. You certainly have good sense, discretion, and God on your side.

Psychology Clinic:
Understanding Your
Inner Motivations

This column is excellent and perceptive every *month, but we have chosen the topic* Having a Negro Friend *as being particularly* timely.

A *reader writes:* "What are the possible advantages and disadvantages of having a Negro for a friend? Please explain."

Answer: The advantages are, of course, obvious. No longer can you be accused of "prejudice" by your racially fanatic acquaintances, especially when many of them barely have a Negro *contact* to call their own.

You will have someone in whom to confide your anxieties and doubts about the present trends in racial matters, and if he is the right kind of friend he will be able to reassure you that it's just the work of a few black militants, that you are still safe from harm, and that the majority of his people are just as much against it as you are.

And you may find some more unique advantages to your friend, as Fred and Martha Rowbottom did.

Fred and Martha owned a house next door to a vacant lot which was suddenly put up for sale. The Rowbottoms wanted to buy that lot but couldn't yet afford it. Then one day when Fred's Negro army buddy and his wife were over, Fred had an inspiration. When the interested party came back to look once more that afternoon, Fred grabbed the basketball. "Quick, Blackie, let's sink a few!" They sauntered outside into the driveway and began to play. And pretty soon the prospective buyers in the car drove away . . . forever.

Where can you find a Negro friend? Almost anywhere. In an army buddy, as Fred did. In a hairdresser, housekeeper, fellow employee, old school friend, yardman; your friendship does not have to be intense . . . or equal.

What are the disadvantages of having a Negro friend?

They are considerably more than first appear. A single personal contact, if not properly understood, can lead to a subtle erosion of attitude. But more about that later. You must first remind yourself that:

1. Your friend is an exception and not like the others; though he may be intelligent and spirited, endowed with humor and style, you know in your heart that most Negroes of *low* intelligence are in jail or on welfare and the smarter ones are meeting somewhere in funny African clothes to plot your demise.

2. It is important not to come in contact with any other "exceptions." Stay away from social-action programs, interracial churches, and other integrated organizations.

3. There are all kinds of tried-and-true, socially ap-

151

152

proved ways of dealing with People of Color; use one of these rather than go off trying to bridge gaps on your disastrous own. Just remember the story of the American who was invited to dinner in an Arabian household and didn't realize you were obliged to belch at the end to show your appreciation of the meal; he couldn't understand why all these people with indigestion kept glaring at him, and consequently he alienated a whole group of friends (who couldn't have been worth much, but that is not the point here).

4. Remember that, underneath it all, Negro people hate whites. Even if your particular friend doesn't seem to hate you, it is in his blood nevertheless. He is only using you. He thinks you can help him get a decent house at a normal price, a job at the place where you work, or an introduction to your friends who can.

So, be careful.

The important thing is to maintain a firm image of the Negro as an abstraction.* You can keep your friend, but carefully. For once you begin thinking that Negroes are individuals with the same emotions, sensitivities, and character failings you have—and deserve to be treated the way you are—you'll have left moderation and sanity far behind.

* See *The Negro Qua Abstraction,* an investigation of Topsy, Aunt Jemima, Uncle Remus, and the Noble Savage.

A Perfectly Terrible Thing That Can Happen and What We Can Do About It

J. J. Uptight's

Editorial of the Year

Ill-boding men have written that, no matter how unassailable our rationalizations and our reactions, somebody someday will plow beneath them all and ask us why we feel the way we feel about *b-l-a-c-k*. Perhaps, they threaten us, we are destined to be the ones who ask ourselves:

WHY?

If that day comes we must be able not only to resist the question; we must be able to resist the answers others have given. People have indicated, for example, that "poor whites," particularly in the South, are kept in place by being told that they have more than the Negroes and therefore should not complain about their lot in life. One folk singer, especially, chants of the rich white telling the poor white that he ought to be happy with the way things are. Now we must strongly remind ourselves that this reasoning applies *only* to that species known as Poor Whites. And we must remind ourselves that *we* certainly are *not* poor whites. *We* are not even lower-middle-class whites, whatever they are. In fact, if most of us could make just a bit more money, and get hold of a slightly bigger house, and cop a few more big positions on our community committees, *we* would be upper-middle-class whites! *We* don't need to feel "better than blacks."

We have no need whatever to know that we live in neighborhoods where Negroes can't live or send our children to colleges they can't afford or attend churches where they don't feel comfortable. We are all perfectly secure about the worth of our identities.

Though most black writers are not presently out to give answers to white folks, their ideas are broadcast loudly enough to be overheard. And these ideas can trouble us if we do not know how to reject them. For example: *

America calling
negroes,
can you dance?
play foot/baseball?

* From Don L. Lee's *Think Black,* copyright © 1967 by Don L. Lee. Reprinted by permission of Broadside Press.

nanny?
cook?
needed now, negroes
who can entertain
ONLY
others not
wanted.
(& are considered extremely dangerous)

How can we reject this absurd poem?

Obviously we are not people who watch football games as though they were dog fights and as though the Negroes were the dogs. We would all just as soon see a big Polack get a broken leg as we would a Negro. We are completely open-minded about the matter. We equally enjoy seeing one color player or another get his guts torn out on the telly.

And are we the kind of people who are made happy by having people available to nanny, cook, or clean for us at the minimum wage (or less) because they can't obtain any other kinds of jobs? Let our "NO!" resound. The intimation that any of us believes in serfdom is a rank and unjust insult perpetrated by those who would undermine our society and attempt to destroy our way of life.

AND

We don't consider anyone dangerous. Each of us knows that our

values for living and our
jobs and our
social status and our

inheritances and
the futures for our children

will hold up *even if everybody and his black and Indian brother has a completely equal opportunity.*

Or do we know that?

No matter. Without doubt we are all the kind of people who can hardly wait to forswear real and imagined securities for the sake of the advancement of other people.

Aren't we all agreed on that?

Sadly we have noticed that some people don't have anything to do but to trouble the consciences of others. It has ever been the position of this periodical that such people ought to be following the Good Book and thinking of things that are pure, just, and holy in the way that we do. But they don't. Not long ago some of these people were at the World Conference on Church and Society and made this statement:

> At this time, racial discrimination appears of greatest immediate danger to humanity. . . . It is often based not only upon fear or resentment of people of another color or tradition but also upon economic self-interest.

So much for them. We have already established that, beneath our rationalizations, whatever feelings we have about *b-l-a-c-k* do not originate with economic interest of any kind.

As for "fear and resentment of other colors and traditions"—the statement is not worth the trouble of discussion. We must only remember when the thought begins to trouble that such fear and resentment are for the man

158

of low caste who is kept ignorant and parochial, the better to be controlled by whoever controls him. And our editorial has already proved—

that none of us is that man.